D0105485

INTERNATIONAL SERIES OF MONOGRAPHS ON PURE AND APPLIED BIOLOGY

Division: **ZOOLOGY**

GENERAL EDITORS: J. E. HARRIS, G. KERKUT AND E. W. YEMM

VOLUME 3

INSTINCTIVE LIVING

By the same author

THE BIOLOGY OF SPIDERS

SPIDERS AND ALLIED ORDERS OF THE BRITISH ISLES

THE ARACHNIDA

MECHANISTIC BIOLOGY AND ANIMAL BEHAVIOUR

THE SPIDER'S WEB

THE LANGUAGE OF SCIENCE

THE WORLD OF SMALL ANIMALS

THE ART OF TRANSLATION

SPIDERS, MEN AND SCORPIONS
(*The History of Arachnology*)

OTHER TITLES IN THE SERIES ON PURE AND APPLIED BIOLOGY

ZOOLOGY DIVISION

Vol. 1. RAVEN—*An Outline of Developmental Physiology.*

Vol. 2. RAVEN—*Morphogenesis : The Analysis of Molluscan Development.*

BIOCHEMISTRY DIVISION

Vol. 1. PITT-RIVERS and TATA—*The Thyroid Hormones.*

BOTANY DIVISION

Vol. 1. BOR—*Grasses of India, Burma and Ceylon.*

Vol. 2. TURRILL—*Vistas in Botany.*

Vol. 3. SCHULTES—*Orchids of Trinidad and Tobago.*

MODERN TRENDS IN PHYSIOLOGICAL SCIENCES DIVISION

Vol. 1. FLORKIN—*Unity and Diversity in Biochemistry.*

Vol. 2. BRACHET—*The Biochemistry of Development.*

Vol. 3. GEREBTZOFF—*Cholinesterases.*

Instinctive Living

A STUDY OF
INVERTEBRATE BEHAVIOUR

by

THEODORE SAVORY

M.A., F.Z.S.

'Animalia corpore parva, mysterio magna.'

PERGAMON PRESS

NEW YORK · LONDON · OXFORD · PARIS

1959

PERGAMON PRESS INC.
122 East 55th Street, New York 22, N.Y.
1404 New York Avenue N.W., Washington 5, D.C.
P.O. Box 47715, Los Angeles, California

PERGAMON PRESS LTD.
4 & 5 Fitzroy Square, London, W.1
Headington Hill Hall, Oxford

PERGAMON PRESS S.A.R.L.
24 Rue des Ecoles, Paris Ve

PERGAMON PRESS Gm.b.H.
Kaiserstrasse 75, Frankfurt-am-Main

Library of Congress Card Number 59–14496

Printed in Great Britain by Kenion Press Ltd., 284 High Street, Slough

CONTENTS

CARISSIMAE
CUIUS SINE AUXILIO
ROGATO COTIDIE COTIDIE DATO
NIHIL AGERE POTUI
AMORIS GRATIAEQUE PLENUS
HUNC LIBRUM PARVUM
D.D.D.

PREFACE

IN THIS book the behaviour of certain invertebrate animals is described and discussed. I have found by experience that the word 'invertebrate' must be emphasized, and that the attention of readers and critics should be directed to it; and this because some of my earlier writings on behaviour have been criticized more than once for containing no references to salivating dogs, maze-threading rats or grain-counting hens. Therefore I repeat the fact that this book is concerned with the behaviour of invertebrate animals only.

Perhaps this will be more clearly understood if I add that one of my intentions in writing it is to develop the thesis that invertebrate behaviour is essentially and fundamentally distinct from vertebrate behaviour.

The spiders and their allies, which have formed the keystone of my practical acquaintance with animal behaviour, have been used as examples wherever they have provided suitable illustration of the point under discussion; and in this respect any zoologist who has read my earlier books may wish to charge me with inconsistency. Such a charge I admit, unrepentant. One of the curiosities of scholarship is that critics are inclined to assume that ideas or interpretations once expressed in print are frozen, and must represent the opinions of the writer for the rest of his life. No active biologist is, in fact, as fossilized as this; it is only the young who are infallible, and in later life we look back with amazement at the assurance and self-confidence that we have lost with the passing of the years. If therefore there should be any who notice that my treatment of my arachnids is less mechanistic than it was twenty years ago, the difference is to be explained partly by changes in the writer's point of view, and partly by the failure of biophysics to make the pertinent contributions that were at one time anticipated by mechanistic biologists.

I wish to express my gratitude to my friend, Mrs. Jean Sexton, and to my secretary, Miss Joan Clark, for their valued help in the preparation of the typescript of this little book.

T. H. S.
Kensington

I

THE ACTIVE INVERTEBRATE

FOUR fundamental reasons, which will help to explain why this book has been written, should be set down at its opening.

First, because the behaviour of an animal is to many biologists one of the most fascinating aspects of its study. However much one may enjoy the outdoor occupation of seeking and collecting, or the laboratory occupations of identifying and dissecting, the observation of the living creature, the simple watching of what it is doing or waiting to see what it will do next, often transcends all other branches of zoology.

Secondly, because of the recognized difficulties of discussing the subject of behaviour. In no part of zoology is it so necessary to give so much attention to the choice of the words in which one tries to describe one's observations and to expound one's interpretations thereof. It is so essential to avoid any appearance of an unjustified teleology, so important to try to present the animal's point of view and not that of the human spectator, that the greatest care in expression is vital. Words whose meanings have been modified by the associations they have acquired may easily give an impression which is not that which the writer wishes to convey, and a continuous straining after an unmistakable clarity must accompany the composition of every sentence. This adds very considerably to the attractiveness of work on all kinds of animal behaviour.

Thirdly, because on its behaviour depends the survival of the animal. All living organisms differ from inanimate objects in that they are constantly doing things, and it is the things they do that make up their lives; or perhaps it may better be said that their lives are the things they do. Therefore we cannot hope to gain more than an incomplete impression of any animal unless we make an attempt to understand its behaviour.

Fourthly, and by far the most important, because a large proportion of the work on animal behaviour has been based on the study of vertebrate behaviour, and in recent years this proportion has shown a tendency to increase. The herring-gull and the three-spined stickleback have usurped the places formerly held by dogs that salivated when bells were rung and rats that made their way through mazes; but there has been little discussion of the relationship between the behaviour patterns of vertebrates and invertebrates. Recently I made an attempt to review the known facts about the behaviour of spiders and other arachnids, with the initial assumption that they would be found to fall into line with the very interesting facts lately described by Dr. N. Tinbergen and Dr. K. Lorenz. I had thought that the valuable concepts of these two eminent ethologists might be supported by the observations that had been made on arachnids; and I hoped that the science of arachnology might acquire merit from its ability to make contributions to the much more popular science of ethology.

My assumption was unjustified, my work was wasted, and my hope disappointed, because, as I now believe, I had sought for principles that were not to be found, and had looked for support that could not be given. The consequence is the present book, the product of that chastening experience. Its central purpose is to advance and to try to justify the thesis that the behaviour of invertebrates is fundamentally distinct from the behaviour of vertebrates; that it ought not to be considered as a simpler or lower or earlier or more primitive form of animal behaviour, nor yet as illustrating in any of its forms the elements from which an apparently, yet doubtfully, more complex or more highly evolved behaviour pattern is composed; but that it is a form of animal activity *sui generis*; and that, to illustrate my contention by a familiar comparison, it is no more possible to understand the behaviour of birds and mammals by doing experiments with worms and insects than it is possible to appreciate the niceties of baseball by sitting in the pavilion above the Senior Turf and watching the First Eleven playing cricket. Therefore it seems to be worth while to seek for both similarities and differences between the capacities of the hollow dorsal nervous system of the vertebrate and the solid ventral nervous system of the invertebrate; to try to compare inherited instinctive reactions with acquired intelligent responses.

* * * *

As I write there stands on my laboratory bench a cage containing a spider. The cage is no more than a rectangular cardboard box with a piece of Perspex as a lid (Fig. 1). A sheet

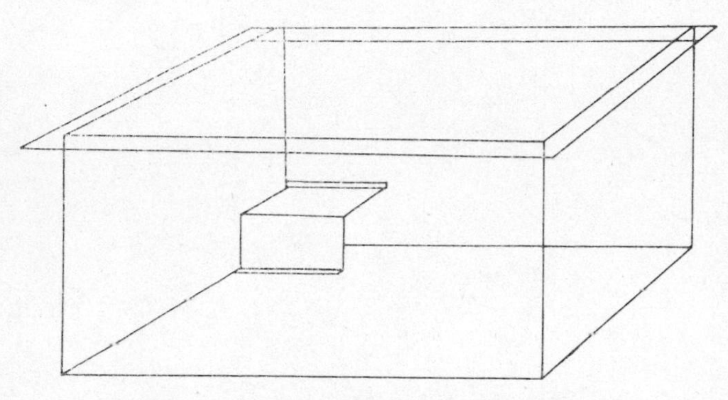

Fig. 1. Cage for house-spider, *Tegenaria.*

of silk is hung like a hammock within it; reaching from side to side and from end to end, it covers almost the whole of the box, and in one corner it is rolled into a tube. Here the silk is thicker than elsewhere, and here the spider rests, as usual, waiting. . . .

The spider is a common house spider, *Tegenaria atrica.* It has been in the box for more than three weeks, and since it makes a nightly addition to the silk sheet, its web is by now a fairly robust piece of tapestry, and a very effective fly-trap.

A fly, an ordinary house-fly, *Musca domestica,* has just been taken from the window pane and put into the cage; it walks a few steps along the side and one of its feet touches a thread of the web. It seems to be a barely noticeable contact, and yet the spider, several inches away, responds at once. It comes out of the tube and stands at its mouth, as if it knew that the chance of another meal had come its way.

But the fly has also responded; it is standing perfectly still, as if it knew that to shake the web again would be a very dangerous thing to do; and so, for perhaps half a minute, the two animals wait, motionless, a trial of patience. They seem to be staring into each other's eyes, but if so they apparently fail to recognize what they see. Few creatures can be more accustomed to wait in patient expectation than spiders, few can be more restless than flies. The fly soon moves again, touching the threads, the spider rushes forward, but by the time it has reached the centre of the disturbance, the fly, unimpeded, has escaped and has flown across the cage.

The spider does not follow it, but goes back to its tube in the corner; and, as it goes, its long spinnerets are seen to be spread apart, trailing silk behind them. On arrival the spider turns round, quite obviously under the influence of some stimulus, takes up a position some little way in advance of its usual resting place. Its four front legs can now be seen to have grasped the web and be pulling on it, for under each foot the silk is raised into a small cone, as if the spider were anxious not to miss the slightest tremor of the sheet.

A second wait ensues, to be ended as before by the fly tripping over the web. The spider's forward rush is quicker, its jaws are open, and the fly, delayed by entanglement with the elastic silk, cannot escape. The end, always inevitable, sees the carrying of the victim to the tube, where it is soon sucked dry.

This short but reasonably accurate account of the events witnessed has been chosen as the opening of this book because it gives, first, an example of the kind of thing that the student of animal behaviour sees, and of the way in which he describes it. It also serves to demonstrate the kind of problem which a scientific interpretation of animal behaviour entails.

* * * *

Like every other branch of science, the study of behaviour depends in the first instance on facts determined by observation and experiment, and it would scarcely be wrong to say that at this stage it is one of the simplest forms of science imaginable. There is usually little difficulty about watching the activities of animals, and little necessity for elaborate equipment or apparatus; while everywhere there are so many animals of so many kinds that opportunities for watching them are not far to seek.

In consequence, natural historians and others have collected a large number of facts, and their observations are always open to confirmation by anyone with the time and patience needed to do so. These observations have been fully and even picturesquely described, and the descriptions themselves have produced the first notes of criticism and disagreement.

Satisfactory descriptions of animal behaviour should supply answers to the questions 'How in these circumstances do these animals behave?' and 'What are the consequences of their behaving as they do?' At the beginning of this chapter an attempt was made to show how this may be done. The reader will notice that the account is moderately lively, that it tries to suggest the dramatic, even the tragic, nature of the events that took place, and that it does not appear to treat the animals as a couple of insensitive machines. To this extent, therefore, it paints a picture of the scene. On the other hand, caution is to be seen in three occurrences of the words 'as if', each of them followed by a phrase which implies mental or perhaps conscious processes on the part of the animals concerned. The importance and value of the two little words 'as if' in descriptions of animal behaviour cannot easily be exaggerated, for they enable the writer to create an atmosphere of feeling, knowing and striving without committing himself to a suggestion that such psychic conditions are really operating, and guiding an animal through its activities. As will be seen later, this is a basic principle in all studies of the behaviour of animals.

The inquisitive biologist, however, is not content with this; he wishes to probe a little more deeply into the matter, to find, if possible, an answer to a third question, 'Why do these animals behave like this?' In other words, he seeks for an interpretation of the facts, just as a chemist, not content with the knowledge that compounds show the regularities expressed in the laws of constant and multiple proportions, wonders why this is so. The chemist for a long time used the hypothesis of the indivisible atom to help him in this matter; the biologist is not so fortunate. Herein lies the fundamental difficulty and much of the interest of the scientific study of behaviour.

There are, in general, two ways of answering questions that begin with the word 'Why?' One is with a statement that immediately suggests another question, and so only pushes the problem back, a step at a time. Why is the fire bright? Because it is hot. Why is it hot? Because it is burning. Why is it burning? Because carbon combines with oxygen. Why does carbon combine with oxygen? Why, indeed? And so on. Any series of Why? questions is likely to end in this unsatisfactory way. The other way in which a Why? question can be answered involves the idea of purpose. Why is the fire burning? Because Joan lit it. Why did Joan light it? In order to warm the author's study. At this point we are satisfied, because we can understand the author's point of view, but, as will be seen, the purpose of an animal's behaviour is not so easily elucidated. Hence the problem of animal behaviour is a problem of interpretation.

* * * *

In the approach to his difficulty the biologist has a choice of four roads:

(i) To describe an animal's actions in terms of conscious or voluntary purpose, of a kind similar to the intentions which familiarly direct the activities of men.

(ii) In an exactly opposite way to admit no kind of consciousness, will or purpose, but to regard the animal as responding automatically to nothing other than stimuli from without and material changes within.

(iii) Denying the animal any aesthetic appreciation of such concepts as goodness, truth and beauty, or any foreknowledge of the goals to which its actions are leading, to make simple, direct records of these actions and of the results which follow from them, and to regard these results as the purpose, in an objective sense, of the behaviour.

(iv) To disregard the results of behaviour, and to try to discover its internal causal factors; that is to say to determine what events in nerves and muscles produce a co-ordinated act of behaviour.

These four methods may be called respectively the Aristotelian, the mechanistic, the teleological and the ethological, and something must be said at once about each.

The first is the old-fashioned anecdotal method of recording the observations of animal behaviour. It is derived from the opinion of Aristotle—that an animal moves only for some purpose of its own, and it is not a method now used by scientific writers. One of the most characteristic examples is contained in a few well-known lines about spiders, written by John Evelyn in *Travels in Italy*: 'I have beheld them instructing the young ones how to hunt, which they would sometimes discipline for not well observing: but when any of the old ones did, as sometimes, miss a leap, they would run out of the field and hide themselves in their crannies, as ashamed, and haply not to be seen abroad for four or five hours after.' It is fairly clear that in these lines the observer's imagination has taken charge and has persuaded him that he has seen things that were not there. No doubt there is much sound biological observation recorded in this manner in the literature of the past, but it is so wrapped up in other matters as to be untrustworthy for present-day purposes.

The second method seeks to avoid every chance of falling into such errors and of being criticised in the same way; and it 'goes too far in the right direction'. It is the method of mechanistic biologists. It states that the actions of an animal are responses to stimuli, are no more than physical and chemical consequences of such stimuli, and are neither determined nor influenced by the feelings or wishes of the animal. These are said to be unknowable and hence are held to be non-existent, so that the animal comes to be regarded as an object indistinguishable from a machine.

Much support has been given to this apparently unpromising view; and mechanism has at all times attracted a proportion of biologists, who believe that a more complete knowledge of the physics and chemistry of an animal's metabolism than we possess at present will enable us at some future date to describe all that an animal does in terms of physical and chemical changes. This view is known as ontological mechanism, and is characterized by the categorical statement that animals are, in a sense, machines; complex perhaps, but, like man-made machinery, containing and controlled by nothing that is not material and measurable.

Other mechanists have pointed out that even if organisms are not pure machines, they can often be helpfully studied as if they were. For example, the rates of an organism's responses to light of changing intensity can be measured. The photochemical effect of light on inanimate matter is well known and is expressed in a simple generalization known as the Bunsen–Roscoe Law which can be put into the form of a quantitative algebraic equation (see page 24). This enables us to compare the observed responses of animals with the responses that would be expected from calculation, and whenever an organism is found to agree with such expectations, it is possible for us to prophesy its behaviour in certain prescribed conditions. This makes it unnecessary to postulate the existence or occurrence of anything other than photochemical control. When, therefore, the idea that organisms behave as if they were machines is thus supported by experiment, the opinion is mechanistic, but is not ontologically so. It is methodological mechanism, and in place of statements about the nature of the organism it is content to suggest that animals behave as machines behave, and that behaviour can be usefully examined by quantitative experiments. Methodological mechanism is, in fact, the customary tenet of the biochemical laboratory. Mechanistic theories are more fully discussed in a later chapter.

The essence of the mechanistic method is a concern with the material events which accompany behaviour; the essence of the third or teleological method is a concern with the purpose of the behaviour. The very word 'purpose' is a dangerous one to use in biology, and its different aspects will be more fully discussed in Chapter VII; the basic principles, however, should be stated here.

Obviously, we can know little or nothing of the subjective purposes within an animal, although we may perhaps justifiably deduce a little in some instances; we are therefore well-advised to concentrate our attention on objective purposes, such as may be deduced from the results or consequences of the behaviour.

Ever since I began, in 1912, to study arachnids I have become well-accustomed to the question 'What is the use of spiders?', and I confess with some shame that it took me a long time to see that the only helpful answer must be given from the point of view of the animal and not that of the enquirer. When this is realized, the answer, both simple and adequate, is 'To make more spiders'. Of course, this is not a peculiarity of spiders only; it is just as true to say that the use, the real biological use, of the horse and the olive-tree (to take as examples the species chosen by Poseidon and Pallas Athene in their famous contest) is to make more horses and more olive-trees. The fact that man can exploit some of the characteristics of horses and olive-trees is little more than fortuitous; it is equally true that *Parascaris megalocephala*, the roundworm, also makes use of horses, but no one ever suggests that the use of horses is to encourage the race of roundworms.

If this view is accepted, it supports the idea that all animal behaviour can be regarded as an adaptation whose value is the contribution it makes to the fundamental purpose of animal life, namely multiplication. But an obvious and undeniable prerequisite of multiplication is the survival, for a time at least, of the individual. An animal is a surprisingly vulnerable object, able to survive only by virtue of, and with the help of, numberless characteristics of its body, among which are the form and functioning of its nervous system. Whenever its behaviour enables it to maintain itself in a 'hostile and not incurious world' its behaviour is an adaptation towards survival, just as much as is the action of its kidneys or its gills. In consequence, the chief concern of the teleological method of studying animal behaviour is with the ways in which survival and multiplication result from it.

There remains to be considered that aspect of the scientific study of behaviour which goes by the name of ethology. This is strictly objective, yet seeks to probe more deeply into the nature of behaviour than can be done by a mere concern with its results. The causes of animal behaviour are sought partly in external stimuli, partly in internal events, and in combinations of both. To an ethologist behaviour is movement, 'the total of movements made by the intact animal', and movement involves activity in nerves and muscles, and also their co-ordination which converts the activity into a piece of behaviour. Neurophysiology is therefore the basis of this method of studying the subject, and it is from the neurophysiologists that progress is to be expected.

Some biologists have criticised the ethological method by saying that it takes no heed of the obvious directiveness of animal behaviour and pays no attention to its subjective side. The ethologists have their own answers to these specific charges, but a more general answer is also important. It is that if any scientist chooses a particular kind of phenomenon, and studies it in the belief and hope that it will lead him to the information he wants, it is both unhelpful and irrelevant to tell him that he has not chosen another. A physiologist who had undertaken a research into the action of the pancreas in digestion would not appreciate being told that he had omitted to consider the diets of refugees.

The truth is that all methods of studying the behaviour of an animal are able to make a contribution to biological knowledge.

Whether a spider is regarded as a skilful and bad-tempered seamstress, or as a sort of living machine, or as a device for converting dead flies into little spiders, or as sensitive system of nerves and muscles is of less importance than that the observers and experimenters who adopt any of these points of view should produce descriptions, results and conclusions which will fall into place in the rising structure of biological science. This book is not concerned to support any one method and to condemn the rest, but to expound the principles of them all and to indicate their achievements and limitations when applied to invertebrate animals.

* * * *

The printed descriptions of the doings of annelids and arthropods have been publishd in a variety of languages and a large number of scientific journals, some of which are not always readily accessible. These descriptions divide themselves very clearly into two groups. In one group there are the general accounts of general habits, written from what may be called the natural historian's point of view. Very often the animals have been watched out of doors or in conditions which approach as closely as possible to their natural circumstances. These accounts are seldom critical; they nearly all bear a close family resemblance to one another, and they very often contain, as it were fortuitously, records or details which supply the very facts needed to fix the isolated description in its place in the wider story of behaviour. They give us, in fact, our first examples of a variety of topics.

The other group is more analytical and contains accounts of experimental work done in a laboratory on animals observed in captivity. When once the opinion has been accepted that captivity does nothing to disturb the animals and falsify the result, these records are most valuable. They are the intellectual offspring of the more general observations, for they have extracted one or two features from it, and investigated them more fully, and repeatedly, under controlled conditions. The relation between the two groups is made plain by the fact that whereas the former is likely to be embellished by photographs and sketches, the latter is more probably illustrated with graphs and diagrams. In any comprehensive account of the actions of a group of animals, both sources of information should be used, with due attention to their different natures and different intentions.

II

THE ACTIVE ENVIRONMENT

ONE of the fundamental characteristics of living organisms, which is emphasised by all biologists, is the closeness of the relationship between the animal or plant and the environment in which it lives; and it must be remembered that although, in a superficial view, the organism is an obviously active member of the partnership, the environment is by no means passive. Changes and events of many kinds are constantly occurring in it; these changes impinge on the organism, and, in its turn, the organism responds. A simple, direct and usually instantaneous response of this kind is usually called a reflex action.

An essential feature of a reflex action is its constancy of response. It has been suggested that one of the first peculiarities which distinguished protoplasm as alive and different from non-living matter was its ability to respond to stimuli in a way that lifeless matter could not imitate. One of the early developments of this must have been the appearance of a tendency to respond to the same stimulus in the same way: responses which were followed by the survival of the organism were favoured; others were eliminated by natural selection, so that the survivors showed in their reflexes that adaptiveness, or helpfulness in the business of living, which remains to this day one of the essentials of reflex behaviour.

The standard definition of a reflex action is 'a neuro-muscular adjustment due to the inherited mechanism of the nervous system'. This definition, which is descriptive of mammalian, or perhaps of vertebrate behaviour, implies that nerves and muscles are necessities; but probably reflex response arose before there was any differentiation of the protoplasm into nerve-cells and muscle-cells, just as it is found today in animals which have no such tissue.

Reflexes are as common in man as in invertebrates. Turn your head towards a window and, holding up a hand-mirror, look at the image of your eyes; the pupils are reduced to small, dark circles. Turn sharply away from the window, moving the mirror, and again look at your eyes; you will see the pupils expanding, probably overdoing it and returning a little towards a smaller size before becoming stationary and larger than they were when your face was towards the window. This adjustment of the muscles of the iris to the intensity of illumination is a familiar example of a reflex action in man—an action that is inborn, invariable, involuntary, unconscious, uncontrollable and adaptive.

The adaptive nature of reflex behaviour, the way in which it is obviously a help in securing the survival of the animal, is well shown by all the invertebrates. For example, a reflex response can easily be produced in an earthworm by gently touching it near its head, when an immediate response will be seen in its tail, a change from the normal cylindrical form to a flattened oval. The value of this response is hidden if the worm is lying on the laboratory bench, but if, as in nature, it is half out of its burrow the muscular action of the hindermost segments presses that part of the body more firmly against the earth. This, combined with the penetration of the setae, makes it almost impossible to pull an earthworm out of its burrow.

Alternatively, the instantaneous response of the crayfish to stimuli is both conspicuous and effective; the sudden flexing of its abdomen drives it rapidly backwards and away from the threat of danger.

It is important to notice that these actions of the earthworm and crayfish are reflexes which are frequently elicited, and which constitute a form of response which occurs regularly, as if there were no possible alternatives; because this is, in fact, one of the most obvious features in the reflex behaviour of many invertebrates. In other words, from among several possible reactions to several possible stimuli there often seems to be a tendency for one particular kind of immediate response to establish itself as a 'first reflex' and to come into action in a wide variety of circumstances.

The spider provides a very good illustration of this. Its body contains very little muscle tissue in the abdomen, which is nearly filled with the digestive glands, the gut and the gonads, and which has only the spinnerets needing muscles to move them, whereas the cephalothorax, the front part of the body, contains the muscles needed to move the jaws, the palpi and all the legs. In consequence, it is no surprise to find that reflex movements of the legs are very frequent; the surprise is to be found in the varied nature of the results which follow.

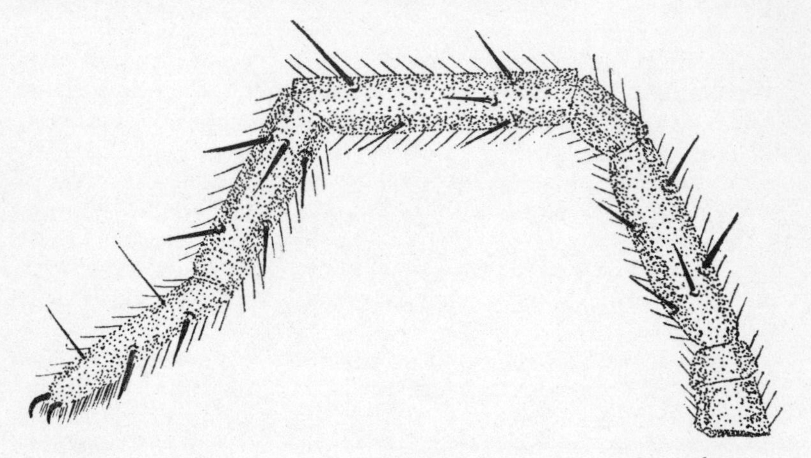

FIG. 2. Leg of a spider, showing spines, setae, and on the tarsus, trichobothria.

The common response of a spider to almost every kind of sudden stimulus is a contraction of the muscle which raises the femur, resulting in a rapid indrawing of the legs. We may call this the 'flexor reflex'.

The course of events may be followed thus. While the spider is at rest the only form of metabolic change affecting the muscles and nerves of the legs is a slow, continuous activity by which the animal preserves its stance. This is sometimes known as a tonic reflex, and some biologists regard it as a form of 'behaviour'. That is to say, they do not limit the meaning of the word behaviour to a change in the type of activity, but extend it to cover all events within the animal's body. Standing still is therefore just as much a form of behaviour as running about or spinning a web.

A sudden stimulus, whatever it may be, upsets the equilibrium, the tonic reflexes give place to others, and the body changes from a state of invisible but balanced activity to a new state of adjustment.

Very often the adjustment is rapid and the muscular action very short-lived. The nervous impulses, however, may continue to discharge and the animal is held motionless in its new position until either the nervous impulses die away or further events provoke a new form of movement. The biologically interesting feature is the survival value of the motionless interim.

Movement is probably the most generally revealing evidence of the presence of living things, to be compared only with odour, which in fact more precisely betrays identity. If a bird-photographer or badger-watcher wishes to be undetected, his first necessity is stillness, and similarly a motionless spider may be overlooked by its enemies or may be mistaken for something else. It is scarcely necessary to repeat the now familiar warning that the old-fashioned description of 'shamming dead' is too generous and too human. The spider is in a state which closely resembles catalepsy.

A cataleptic spider lying in a white dish on a laboratory bench looks, no doubt, like a dead spider; but in nature cataleptic spiders do not lie in such situations, and in their normal surroundings they look like nothing at all. There is no better example of this than the British sand-dune spider, *Philodromus fallax,* which becomes absolutely invisible when, ceasing to run, it crouches motionless against the sand.

There are also examples of spiders in which the femora are brighter than the other leg-segments, and when the flexor reflex suddenly hides them the effect is like that of the 'flash-colouring', well known as a protective device among tree frogs. The eye of the predator is concentrated on the moving colour, and its sudden disappearance disturbs the course of the attack.

The biological interest of all these examples is great. They represent forms of reflex action in which the emphasis falls heavily on the adaptive character of the behaviour, which contributes generously to the animal's chances of survival. Vertebrate reflexes such as coughing or sneezing, or the opening and shutting of the iris already mentioned, have very seldom anything like the same survival value.

On the other hand, a closer parallel with vertebrate reflexes can be seen. The widespread flexor reflex may be regarded as the easiest response to make whenever a more specific type of action is not required, the quickest and the most direct way in which to discharge the extra flood of 'nervous energy' that follows the stimulation of the sense organs. If this is so, it closely resembles human laughter. The precise cause of the conscious realization of the humour in any situation has long been a matter of discussion, but there is little doubt that, conscious humour apart, spontaneous laughter arises whenever there is a demand for a quick release of nervous tension by no particular method. I do not wish to go so far as to suggest that a spider laughs by drawing up its legs, even though the suggestion is clearly less foolish than its sounds; but it illustrates, by a parallel, something of the nature of the action.

* * * *

The 'first reflex' of scorpions is sufficiently interesting to deserve a paragraph. A scorpion is armed with a sting in its active tail, and any occasion which seems to threaten it is at once met by the counter-threat of a sting. The tail, which properly is not a tail at all but is the last six segments of the abdomen, is reared up and the sting thrust rapidly forwards. A scorpion does not sting backwards as a wasp does, but forwards with the sting above its head, probably reaching and piercing a captive that has been seized in the pedipalpi. This stinging reflex can be provoked by circumstances which have nothing to do with a struggling victim or a formidable enemy; it is elicited, for example, when a scorpion is being chloroformed, and it has been seen when the heat of the sun has fallen, through a lens, on the scorpion's back. This is interesting. The old legend that a scorpion commits suicide when surrounded by fire has sprung from the violent thrusts of the sting that are produced as the unlucky animal dies from the heat.

The wind-scorpions, or camel-spiders, of the order Solifugae, are not venomous and their reaction to disturbance is apparently useless. They also raise the abdomen, until it is carried erect, at right angles to the cephalothorax, and like scorpions they show this reaction as they are being anaesthetized, or when they are drowning in alcohol. Zoologists who have been lucky enough to see Solifugae in their natural surroundings have reported a recognizable resemblance to scorpions; perhaps therefore the sudden but useless raising of the abdomen is a form of mimicry. Either the non-venomous Solifugae gives the impression of being a formidable scorpion, or both creatures benefit by sharing a form of behaviour which carries with it a threat of ferocity.

* * * *

The fundamental segmentation of the invertebrate body is responsible for the fact that a reflex action may be carried out by the parts of one segment only, or by two neighbouring segments, or by a group of segments. The progress of the earthworm, for example, in which waves of compression and expansion are communicated from segment to segment, illustrates this, as the stimulus for contraction is passed along the body. So, too, a spider may hold up or withdraw one pair of legs, or two pairs, or four pairs. Hence it often occurs that reflex actions may be shown by parts of an animal, and they may be said to continue after death. Many a young biologist has been surprised to find that the removal of the pericardium from the heart of a frog is followed by a resumption of the rhythmical beating of the organ. This may be maintained for several minutes, even when no steps are taken to prolong it. An observation of this kind shows that death does not occur simultaneously throughout a body, and that the normal vital activities of some regions may outlast their departure from others.

It is otherwise with severed parts. According to some accounts an insect may be cut into three pieces and the thorax will walk away from its own head and abdomen. This action may be regarded as understandable if it is pointed out that important nerve ganglia are contained in the thorax, as well as a proportion of blood sinuses, so that responses of this simple and long-engrained type may not be altogether unexpected. But such a view as this cannot be taken of separated limbs, no longer in communication with the central nervous system, and among the crustaceans and arachnids separated limbs are common enough, the results of the process of autotomy. No doubt one of the most familiar examples of this sort of behaviour is the curious spasmodic twitching which is so often shown by a harvestman's leg after it has been pulled off. At one time this twitching was described as phenomenon that had established itself because of its survival value. The theory was that a predator caught the harvestman by a leg which was instantly shed, and while the predator was occupied in subduing the struggles of the solitary limb, the harvestman was taking the opportunity of escaping to safety on the seven legs that remained.

I do not know whether this little drama has ever been watched by an observer, or whether the whole story is an imaginative reconstruction of events that may have occurred; but I do know that sometimes, when I have been searching for harvestmen, I

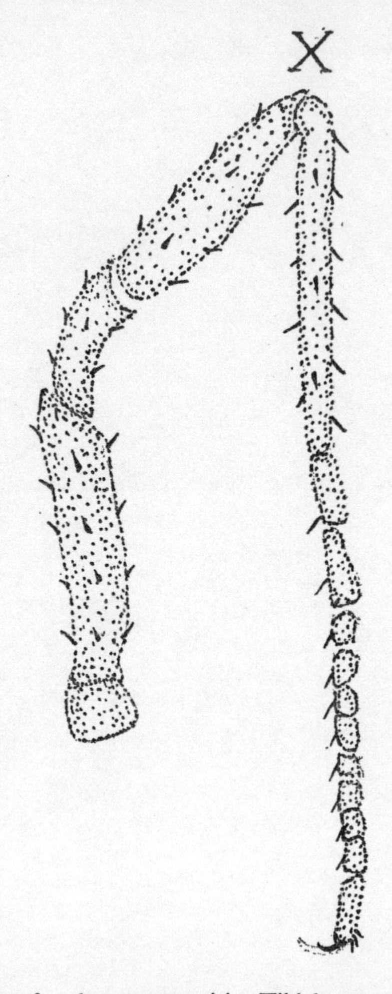

FIG. 3. Leg of a harvestman. X: Tibial-metatarsal joint at which sporadic flexing of a separated leg occurs.

have come upon one of their legs lying quite alone on the ground and steadily flexing at the metatarsal-tibial joint (Fig. 3). It is a sight that is weird enough to have inspired the popular teleological account. Yet of course the most remarkable feature of these kickings is the fact, already mentioned, that the solitary leg, unlike the six legs of the trisected insect, is no longer in communication with the chief ganglia of its nervous system. The consequence of this is that although the isolated limb may well be receiving stimuli from the contact of many of its setae with the ground, it cannot also be receiving impulses from its co-ordinating nerve-centres. Hence the customary 'theory of the reflex arc' breaks down here, and the movements of the leg cannot be 'neuro-muscular adaptation'. It must more closely resemble the purposeless or valueless beating of the frog's heart, and the external stimuli must provoke responses directly in the tissues of the leg.

A very important type of elaboration of reflex actions is found in behaviour of the kind described as a chain-reflex. Here there is a series of reflexes which form a co-ordinated whole, but in which each separate act has its own stimulus and appears inevitably in response to it. The textbook example of this is very often the behaviour of one of the hunting-wasps, which carry out the operation of making or digging a nest, catching caterpillars or spiders, stinging them so as to paralyse them, carrying them to the nest, laying an egg in their bodies, and finally sealing the nest.

I think that a very much better example of chain behaviour is given in Homann's description of the actions of the spider *Evarcha falcata* in catching a fly. The spider belongs to the family of jumping-spiders, Salticidae, known to possess the keenest vision. The arrangement of its eyes is as follows. There is a front row, consisting of two large median eyes, called the direct eyes, and two smaller lateral eyes. Behind this row is a group of four eyes, distinguished as the posterior median eyes and the posterior lateral eyes.

The sequence of events may be described thus. The prey is perceived first by the posterior lateral eyes (Fig. 4), which have a very wide field of vision, but no reaction follows on the part of the spider if the fly does not move. The movement of an image across the retina of a posterior lateral eye stimulates the spider to turn its body towards the moving object, and as a result an image now forms in an anterior lateral eye. Turning continues, and images are now formed in both anterior lateral eyes, and of course in the direct eyes as well. The stimulation of both the

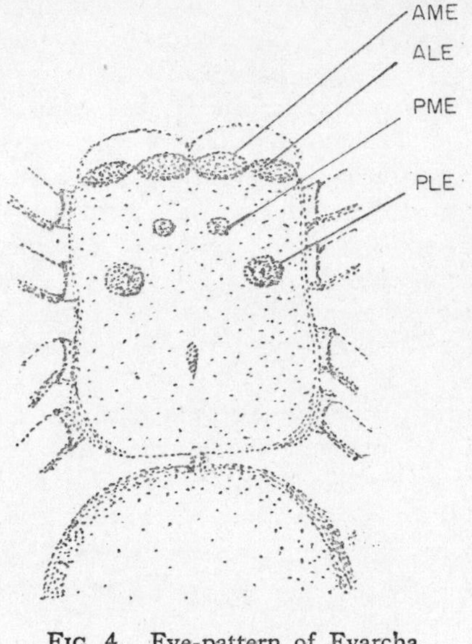

FIG. 4. Eye-pattern of Evarcha.
AME, Anterior median eye
ALE, Anterior lateral eye
PME, Posterior median eye
PLE, Posterior lateral eye.

anterior lateral eyes produces a binocular vision, endowed with some degree of perception of distance. The spider is now in a position to advance towards its prey.

It will be seen from the above that the turning of the spider's body apparently takes place in two stages, first when an image is formed in a posterior lateral eye and later when that image is transferred to an anterior lateral eye. This interpretation is a result of Homann's successful technique for temporarily covering any eye or eyes with a drop of black wax, applied with an electrically warmed needle. He found that if the anterior lateral eyes were covered, the second stage of the turning did not occur. The image moved from the posterior lateral eye, but since it did not appear on the anterior lateral eye, turning stopped and the spider did not catch its prey. The same thing would happen in nature if the insect flew away.

By the time that the image is producing clear vision in an anterior lateral eye, it falls simultaneously on a direct eye. This is an essential in the spider's behaviour, since a moving object which produced images in all the anterior eyes is a stimulus which makes the spider move forwards. The direct eyes enable the spider to perceive something of the form of its prey, although they cover only a small field in its neighbourhood. This is a consequence of the peculiar structure of the visual cells in these eyes, and if the anterior lateral eyes are covered a spider easily loses sight of its victim.

On a closer approach to the object, the better definition given by the direct eyes seems to be the determining factor in the spider's behaviour. At a distance of 5 or 6 cm a male Evarcha will begin courtship if the object approached is another spider of the same family. If the spider approaches something that does not possess this particular form, it begins to stalk it by the slowest possible forward movements, treating it as a prey and not as a mate.

At a distance of 2 or 3 cm a courting male Evarcha acts as if it can distinguish between a female of its own species and another male or a member of another genus, which it had been courting 'by mistake'. It will continue its solicitation of the female, but cease courtship otherwise. At 1·0 or 1·5 cm it leaps upon and bites its victim. It is of importance to observe that if the anterior lateral eyes are covered the spider will leap upon a fly from a slightly greater distance, a fact which seems to be related to the greater resolving power of the direct eyes.

The general result of Homann's work is to make it clear that each pair* of eyes has one special function in providing a stimulus for a particular movement; and that normally each response is followed by the next to give an appearance of continuity in the behaviour. Yet by experiment, with a droplet of wax, the chain may be broken at any point.

* * * *

This discussion of reflex actions should not be brought to an end without a reference to the phenomenon of the conditioned response, established by Pavlov and too well-known to call for a

* The posterior median eyes, not mentioned in the above account, receive impressions from objects behind the spider.

description here. The question has often been asked, How far down the animal kingdom can behaviour of this sort be found? The answer in general seems to be that conditioned reflexes can be established in vertebrates, but that there are few accounts of experimental work in which experimental biologists have chosen invertebrate animals for this purpose.

III

DIRECTED MOVEMENTS

ONE OF the most obvious features of nearly all animals above the level of the Coelenterata is their bilateral symmetry, and it is generally supposed that the advantages which are the consequences of this kind of bodily construction have been partly responsible for the success of the Triploblastica. An important accompaniment is the same symmetrical arrangement of the sense-organs, so that the familiar placing of the two eyes, two ears and two nostrils of man is repeated and multiplied in the placing of the more numerous ocelli, setae and other receptors on the bodies and limbs of the crustaceaus, insects and arachnids.

There is here an opportunity for an elaboration of the reflex responses which normally follow the stimulation of a sense-organ, and which were described in the preceding chapter. Asymmetrical stimulus may produce unequal responses in the two sides of the body, and the result may be a turning of the latter or a deviation of its course. A response of this kind was first called a tropism.

The concept of a tropism is due to A. P. de Candolle, 1788–1841, a botanist, who used the word in 1835 to describe the turning movements of plants in response to the light of the sun. This was known as heliotropism or phototropism, and was soon followed by geotropism, a turning towards the force of gravity, and by hydrotropism, a turning towards the source of water. These twistings of the stems and petioles of plants, a consequence of different permeability and different turgor-pressure in their cells, these slow burrowings of roots, a consequence of cell-division and growth, are clearly different from the so-called tropisms of animals. The two kinds of response bear an outward resemblance, especially when the animal happens to be a sedentary one like a hydroid; but ordinary active animals which turn aside from a straight line as a result of one-sided stimulation are showing a type of response which is more intelligibly described as a directed reflex. A different vocabulary should therefore be used in discussing their behaviour, and this has been produced by changing -tropism into -taxis. Thus the swimming of a small animal towards the light has been called positive phototaxis, consistent upward climbing is negative geotaxis, and so on. This is a useful distinction, although it will be seen in the next chapter that it has been partly replaced in its turn by another system.

The most familiar example of phototactic movement in animals is undoubtedly the flight of the moth to the lamp. This apparent attracion ends often enough in serious or fatal singeing and so cannot possibly be described as instinctive. Instinctive actions, as the zoologist understands them, seldom lead to self-destruction. On the other hand, the behaviour presupposes a connection of an irresistible nature between the stimulation of the visual cells and the contractions of the wing-muscles. The course of events is believed to be somewhat as follows. Light, falling on the eyes, produces certain photochemical changes, and the compounds thus formed diffuse through the body. They are assumed to be of a kind that affects the tone of the muscles, including those of the wings or legs. If, therefore, the eyes of one side of the body are more brightly illuminated than the eyes of the other side, there may be expected to be a greater concentration of these photochemical products on one side, followed by an in-drawing of the legs or by a hastening or a slowing of the beating of the wings to correspond. This must be followed by a turning of the animal as it runs, crawls or flies, until both eyes are equally illuminated, and balanced limb-movements carry it forwards. All this is quite independent of thoughts or wishes; thus the supporters of the tropism theory of animal conduct say that an animal goes not where it wants to go, but where its limbs take it.

It is to be observed that the basis of this argument is a chemical one. Photochemistry is an exact science, which has been studied for many years, and in their simplest manifestations photochemical reactions are found to follow a generalization known as the Bunsen–Roscoe Law. This states that the amount of any substance produced in a photochemical reaction is proportional to the intensity of the light and to the time of exposure. Expressed in algebraic form, the law's equation is

$$Q = k \, . \, it,$$

where Q is the amount of product, i is the intensity of illumination and t the duration of the exposure.

The value of a law of this kind is that it makes possible a direct experimental investigation of phototactic behaviour. A single example will make this clear and will demonstrate the nature of the conclusions to which a series of such experiments will lead.

Imagine a group of small animals recently hatched from the same batch of eggs. They will have much the same inherited qualities, be of the same age, and will have passed the whole of their lives in the same conditions. They will be therefore as nearly alike as is possible, and will form a homogenous group likely to react uniformly. However, individual differences are certain to exist, so that in all experiments the whole group must be used and a chance given to these variations to cancel each other. Let it be further supposed that light 'attracts' or 'repels' these animals, that is to say it stirs them from a state of rest and makes them creep towards or away from its source. Imagine, lastly, that the group, while resting, is exposed to the light of a lamp placed one metre from them.

Gradually they will respond, though not all at the same rate, and after a certain interval half of them will have travelled a distance of one centimetre towards (or away from) the lamp. Suppose that this interval of time is twelve minutes. If the lamp were to be moved to a distance of two metres, the intensity of illumination on the animals would be reduced to a quarter of its former value, at three metres to one-ninth, and so on. This is the familiar Law of Inverse Squares. Therefore a repetition of the experiment, with the lamp placed at two metres, would be expected to produce the same movement of half the animals through one centimetre each in $12 \times 4 = 48$ minutes; at three metres in $12 \times 9 = 108$ minutes. These expected figures can be compared with those actually found in experiments.

If the agreement between the two sets of figures is close enough to be significant, as in practice it often is, it suggests that the animals react to the light exactly as a photosensitive compound would do, and hence it may be assumed that their movements were only the outcome of photochemical reactions. and nothing else.

If this is so, it becomes possible to predict the behaviour of the animals, at least statistically, wherever the lamp may be placed—e.g. at 1·5 metres the same effect would be found after $12 \times (1{\cdot}5)^2 = 27$ minutes.

A mechanistic biologist would now conclude that since the animals' behaviour is predictable in terms of photochemistry, there is no need to assume that such behaviour is instigated by mental processes acting teleologically: i.e. by a mind directing it towards the attainment of a desirable result. The general acceptability of such a conclusion will be discussed later.

This example of phototactic behaviour has been useful for two reasons. First, it makes clear the important fact that tactic or tropistic actions are concerned with the orientation of the animal's body in relation to certain external stimuli. Thus taxes may be defined both briefly and accurately as 'directed reflexes'.

Secondly, it makes clear the advantages which light has over other stimuli in experimental work on behaviour. A beam of light can be easily arranged in any direction and its intensity can be precisely controlled. Light is known to produce chemical changes, and the rates of these changes are predictable. In consequence, a large proportion of the work on taxes has been concerned with light, and has often succeeded in giving consistent accounts of behaviour in terms of physics and chemistry. Other kinds of tactic behaviour must, however, be described before a general discussion is possible.

* * * *

Just as the movements of animals towards or away from light seem to bear a resemblance to the positive or negative heliotropism of plant organs, so other tendencies may be compared to the familiar plant movements called geotropism, hydrotropism or chemotropism. For example, every naturalist knows that the larvae of some butterflies climb upwards when about to pupate, while others as persistently move downwards and bury themselves in the ground. These actions may be described as geotaxes, for it appears that nothing other than the force of gravity determines the larva's choice of direction, up or down.

Equally familiar is the fact that frogs and toads, awakening in spring from hibernation, make their way to the nearest water for breeding, and this may be called hydrotaxis. Again the elementary text-books tell us that fern antherozoids are directed to the archegonia by the malic acid secreted by the latter; this is chemotaxis, and the word might equally well describe the flight of the bee towards nectar and pollen.

When once there is established the habit of calling any constant or habitual form of behaviour by the name of a taxis or tropism determined by some particular type of stimulus, and when once the habit appears to be justified, it becomes surprisingly easy to multiply examples of tropistic behaviour and to extend them to include almost everything that any animal does. Simple and familiar habits may thus be labelled; for instance, a cockroach is normally to be found in a crevice or crack and is described as showing stereotropism or an innate tendency to bring the body as fully as possible into contact with solid surfaces; an animal turns its head upstream in water and so swims against the current or turns upwind in the air and flies against the breeze and these actions are described respectively as rheotropism and anemotropism, caused by an equalizing of fluid or air-pressures on the two sides of the body. This shows that the word tropism has become little more than a label used to denote movements of the body and concerned with its orientation.

One of the surprises in the study of animal behaviour is the length of the list of 'tropisms' which have been thus named by biologists at different times and in different countries. The following list contains thirty-six and may not be complete:

aerotropism	exotropism	phototropism
anemotropism	galvanotropism	plagiotropism
branchiotropism	gamotropism	rheotropism
chemotropism	geotropism	selenotropism
chromotropism	haptotropism	sinistrotropism
cytotropism	heliotropism	sitotropism
dexiotropism	histotropism	stereotropism
dextrotropism	hydrotropism	thermotropism
diageotropism	hygrotropism	thigmotropism
diaheliotropism	neurotropism	trophotropism
diaphototropism	paraheliotropism	tropotropism
electrotropism	parasitotropism	vibrotroism

A perusal of this quaint vocabulary suggests certain observations on the words it contains.

1. Some of them are synonyms—e.g. electrotropism and galvanotropism; stereotropism and thigmotropism.

2. Some of them are nearly synonyms—e.g. heliotropism, selenotropism and phototropism. These three are concerned with light; the light of the sun, the light of the moon, and light in general as opposed to darkness. Response to moonlight is sufficiently rare to be neglected in a general account, but several writers have drawn a distinction between the effects on behaviour of sunlight and diffused daylight. Many jumping-spiders, for example, are active hunters while the sun is shining, but as soon as it is hidden by a cloud they disappear into hiding. They might therefore be described as heliopositive and photonegative.

In the same way, hydrotropism refers to movements into liquid water, while hygrotropism implies a choice of moist air in preference to dry air, a feature common to many invertebrates.

3. Some of them are peculiar in so far as they refer to stimuli which are unlikely to fall on animals in natural circumstances. The most obvious of these is electrotropism, for wild animals but rarely run up against electric currents and find themselves being drawn either to anode or cathode. But an electric current resembles a beam of light in that it can readily be changed both in intensity and direction; as a result it has attracted the experimental zoologist, and laboratory responses to electricity have been recorded for many animals, from Paramecium to eels.

4. Some of them are far-fetched, not to say hypothetical, existing more definitely in the opinion of the observer than in the behaviour of the animal. Branchiotropism, for example, is defined as a tendency in fishes to seek water containing a sufficiency of dissolved oxygen; thermotropism is a coming to rest in surroundings that are neither too hot nor too cold.

5. Some of them are almost wholly confined to animals of one particular kind and so have very little general interest. Thus vibrotropism or the response of spiders to vibrations of their webs is a habit limited to web-spinners.

6. Some of them are not tropisms at all, in anything like the sense in which the word is properly applied. Histotropism is said to be shown by internal parasites when they attach themselves to the particular tissue on which they normally rest or feed. Sitotropism is a peculiar name for seeking food.

* * * *

On many occasions the path taken by an animal may be a result of two taxes which reinforce each other; for example, positive geotaxis and negative phototaxis may together drive it downwards. Alternatively, two taxes may oppose each other, and the animal may appear to yield to the stronger. Again the position is one that is familiar to the botanist, who has given the zoologist a lead: the roots of plants tend to grow downwards and to grow towards water, and in natural circumstances these directions are usually the same. But most students of elementary biology can recall the fact that if beans are sown in a sieve of moist earth their roots first penetrate the meshes and then turn and grow upwards, re-entering the wet earth (Fig. 5). This is taken as

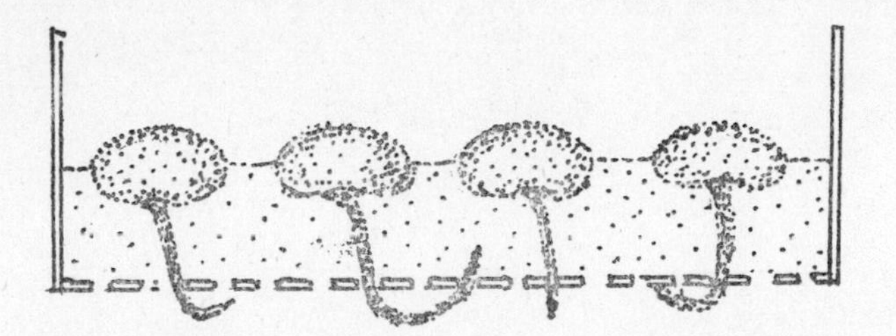

Fig. 5. Demonstration of the superiority of hydrotaxis over geotaxis in bean radicles. The young roots, having grown downward into the air, turn up and grow into the moist sawdust.

a demonstration that hydrotropism is stronger than geotropism. In the same way, animals that are stereotactic are often photonegative; and some species of the polychaete worm Nereis will enter and remain in illuminated glass tubes even though the light proves fatal, because their stereotaxis is so much the stronger.

The development of this idea is obvious. An animal in nature meets many different stimuli to which it responds tropistically or tactically; so that we may look upon it as being subjected to an interplay of taxes, some reinforcing each other, some in opposition, and the animal compulsorily obedient to their algebraic sum. Here is a position which the mechanist greets enthusiastically, for it suggests a multitude of experiments in which a suitable animal is observed and possibly the angle through which it turns is measured, when it is under the influence of stimuli from two sources.

In the first and simplest cases the two stimuli may be of the same kind, for example, the light from two lamps. It is found that if a photonegative animal is made to approach the line joining two sources of light it will cross this line at right angles if the intensities of illumination are the same on its two sides; but if they are unequal it will cross this line at an angle which is proportional to the distances between it and the lamps. This is true tactic behaviour, in direct contrast to the action of an intelligent human being. 'A man, wandering at night across a dark countryside and perceiving in the distance the lights of two cottages, would direct his steps towards one of them'.

Alternatively, the two stimuli may be of different kinds. There is a planarian worm, *Leptoplana variabilis,* which is negatively phototactic and cathodically galvanotactic; it may be placed in a

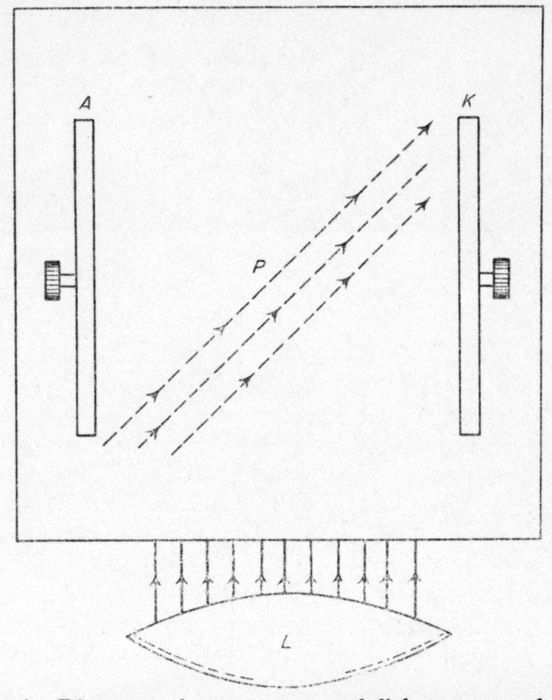

FIG. 6. Diagrammatic arrangement of light-source and electrodes, showing path taken by Leptoplana equally directed towards the cathode and away from the light.
A=anode; *K*=cathode; *L*=lens; *P*=path taken.

dish of water with an electrode at each end and a lamp at one side. In the dark it moves to the cathode; if the current is not flowing it moves away from the light (Fig. 6). Both current and illumination can be varied, and it is found that the planarians move at an angle of 45° to the directions of both stimuli when the current density is proportional to the logarithm of the intensity of illumination.

This is an unexpected, not to say an elaborate, relationship, the physiological interpretation of which is not easy, but is just the kind of mathematical result that workers on tactic behaviour try to obtain; for when it is done the behaviour of the animal can be reduced to a formula. Thus, in the case of Leptoplana, the Bunsen–Roscoe law, already quoted, tells the mechanist that the amount of photochemical product made in the animal's body is given by the equation $Q_1 = k_1 . it$. The experiment outlined above shows that the quantity Q_2 of the electrochemical product is given by the equation $Q_2 = k_2 \log i$. If the worm's line of movement bisects the angle between the stimuli, then

$$Q_1 = Q_2$$

$$k_1\, it = k_2 \log i$$

$$K = \frac{k_1}{k_2} = \frac{\log i}{it}$$

The deduction that follows from this is important; it is nothing less than the assertion that the value of K can be used to predict the behaviour of the animal over a range of illumination and current; and this is the essential function of a scientific law deduced from measurements.

Further, it is a logical extension of this to suppose that a sufficient number of such experiments would make it possible to compare the effects of other stimuli, such as the force of gravity or the smell of ammonia, with each other and with the influence of light. When this was completed the behaviour of the animal would be predictable however complex were the environment in which it was placed, or however numerous the stimuli to which it was subjected.

In consequence, there need be no surprise that biologists such as Loeb have supported the Tropism Theory of Animal Conduct, and have sought to explain all that an animal does in terms of external stimuli and directed response. The theory has a simplicity which is superficially attractive; it is the outcome of quantitative experimental work: it suggests many more such experiments; and its findings can be easily expressed in a characteristic and not unattractive vocabulary.

When, however, the attempt is made to expand these ideas into a comprehensive theory, which shall include the behaviour even of man, then it fails to carry conviction. A tropism is not a material object, a thing which may fall upon or develop within a weed, a worm or a workman; it is a way in which plants and some animals react to external stimuli. A little consideration suggests that experiments on tactic behaviour are really measurements of the reactions of the sense organs and the responses of the muscles; it may be useful, perhaps it may be necessary, to know the facts about these actions, but their relations to any psychic events are obscure, and experiment tells us nothing about this.

The tactic view of behaviour may be criticized thus—it is manifestly illogical for an experimental biologist to ask whether animals that lurk under stones do so for some conscious reason, and then to give a negative answer merely because the taxes which guide them there have been recognized and described.

IV

KINESES AND TAXES

It is one thing to criticize the Tropism Theory so destructively as to leave the impression that only with respect to light has it really been able to offer us a fair picture of an animal's movements, and quite another thing to put in its place a more adequate method of classifying invertebrate behaviour in a constructive and helpful way. Yet if animal behaviour is to justify its place as a recognized subscience or branch of biology this is an essential. There must be found some sort of order in our observed facts, or there will be no secure basis on which to found our hypotheses and from which to advance to a better understanding of the whole.

In the list of 'tropisms' given in the last chapter there was included the form of behaviour known as chemotropism or chemotaxis. This name was applied to forced movements induced by the direct action of some chemical compound, causing an animal to move towards or away from the potent compound in question. Familiar examples are the flight of the wasp into the marmalade and the running of cockroaches to alcohol, movements which are carried out with such a persistence that inevitably the incautious observer says that the insects are chemopositive to the substance in question. Conversely, the optimism with which we try to repel the clothes moth with naphthalene or *p*-dichlorobenzene may be founded on a believe that the moth is chemonegative to these compounds.

A special case of chemotaxis is seen in hydrotaxis, a form of behaviour in which the animal is impelled to move towards water; another is seen in hygrotaxis, where the tendency is to seek a moist, or a dry, atmosphere.

These and several other so-called taxes share an important feature, which is that the stimuli, normal components of the environment, do not act with appreciably different intensities upon symmetrically placed sense organs, but pervade or permeate the neighbourhood of the animal. In consequence, the external stimuli do not lend themselves to experimental treatment as readily as does light.

In place of the turning movements characteristic of true tropisms there is to be observed in the animals a tendency to move along a gradient of concentration towards a greater or a smaller concentration of some atmospheric vapour, whether it be odorous, like naphthalene, or odourless, like water; or, as an alternative, there is a tendency to come to rest in an atmosphere in which a significant component is present in some definite proportion. For example, a 'thirsty' cockroach tends to come to rest in air at a lower temperature than is usual for it. The normal temperature, or the 'indifference-zone' is 20°—29°C, but D. L. Gunn (13)* showed that a cockroach dried to 70% of its weight chooses 12°—23°C. He described this as a response to a gradient of saturation deficiency; an avoidance of air of higher evaporating-power.

It is reasonable to assume that such animals show an inclination to remain at rest in an atmosphere with which their bodily tissues are in a condition of equilibrium, or, to put it in psychological terms, to stay where they are most comfortable. This does not necessarily imply that an animal is consciously comfortable in the same way as is a man in an easy chair in front of his study fire. It implies rather that a physical condition produces a state which is the objective parallel of comfort, or a condition which does not impel the animal to move into a situation where the conditions are different.

These considerations, and others, have led Fraenkel and Gunn (12) to work out a new system of describing animal behaviour, or a new way of classifying the different kinds of movements that animals make. In this method movements are divided into:

1. kineses
2. taxes.

Kineses are defined as the effects exerted by stimuli on the rate of random movements, such as are sometimes called trial and error

* The references are to the Bibliography, following Chapter 9.

movements. In affecting the rate and not the direction of movement, kineses are clearly distinguished from taxes. When there is no more than a simple effect on the rate of locomotion, related to the intensity of the stimulus, the behaviour is described as an orthokineses: when the effect appears as a change in the frequency of turning, or rate of change of direction, the behaviour is described as a klinokineses. Trial and error movements have also been called phobotaxes, but the name kineses is to be preferred, because it does not suggest a conscious questing on the part of the animal and it is also free from the human association of the word phobia.

Taxes, on the other hand, are orientated movements resulting from responses to the direction from which the stimulus arrives. They normally depend on the existence of symmetrically-placed paired sense-organs, and they result in an animal's following a path related to and determined by the direction of the source of the stimulus. These taxes, or tactic movements, fall into five groups:

1. KLINOTAXIS. This is a simple orientation movement due to a comparison between intensities of stimulation on the two sides of the animal, following lateral deviations of the body, or a part of the body, from a straight line. Klinotaxis may appear in unexpected circumstances. For example, if a blow-fly larva is crawling beneath an electric lamp, and the light is switched on whenever it begins to move towards the left, it will change its direction, and so crawl, in effect, in a circle to the right. Therefore, in this case, the orientation of the animal is not due to the direction of the light, but is due to different intensities of two stimuli received one after the other.

2. TROPOTAXIS. This is an orientation movement which depends on a comparison between intensities of stimulation on the sides of an animal, but, unlike klinotaxis, the stimuli act simultaneously on the sense-organs. There is no deviation in course, as orientation follows directly. This is, in effect, the pure 'tropism' of Loeb, and all the well-characterized examples of tropistic movements, in the sense that he used, should be classified in this group. They can always be tested or investigated by experiments with two sources of stimulation, and observation of the animal's enforced route between them.

3. TELOTAXIS. This is an orientation movement towards the source of one stimulus, which acts as if it were a goal or an end

to be sought. Telotactic movements have therefore an outward appearance of purpose, for there is little or no deviation in the path taken by the animal.

It has been said by some writers on behaviour that true telotaxis is shown only in the movements of animals towards, or away from, the light. But there can be no doubt that the scope of the category should be broadened to include vibrotaxis. This is shown when a web-spider runs across its vibrating web to the entangled and struggling insect which the web has captured. In this action the approach to the victim has every appearance of being a purposeful approach to a goal, and there is no deviation in the path taken by the spider.

At the same time it should be recalled that when vibrotaxis was first recognised by W. M. Barrows (1) in 1915, he described the result of simultaneously oscillating the web at two foci, when the spider took a path between them. This is typical tropotaxis, and the fact of its existence only shows the imperfection of classification—so common an occurrence in science of all kinds.

4. Menotaxis. This is a modified form of telotaxis, of which it may be described as a special case. It is a movement in which there is maintained a constant angle between the direction of the stimulus and the path of the animal. The most familiar instance is probably the route of the home-going ant, which finds its way by reference to the sun, taking a path always equally inclined to the incident light.

5. Mnemotaxis. This is movement in a direction determined by memory, and is familiarly shown by worker bees, which remember the situation of their hive.

* * * *

Clearly this arrangement of the observed facts of orientation is more complex than the simple idea of the tropism or taxis. This is as it should be. Animal behaviour is not a simple phenomenon, and cannot be described and understood in simple terms. The variety of the kineses aand taxes has the advantage that it avoids both the necessity and the temptation to stretch the single conception of 'tropistic movement' over the whole range of animal behaviour.

The essence of the difference between kineses and taxes is perhaps most easily understood by considering the case of movements determined by the force of gravity. An animal which habitually moves upwards or downwards does so because somehow its sense organs react to the pull of the earth; the resulting movement shows a discrimination between 'up' and 'down', which is a response to, or a realization of, the direction of the stimulus. This is pure geotaxis. As the animal climbs up (or down) the intensity of the stimulus, that is, the familiar *g*, the magnitude of the force, does not alter by an amount that is appreciable. Therefore the animal does not tend to move more and more quickly as it approaches the top (or the bottom) of a tree-trunk. If it did so, it would be illustrating or exhibiting geokinesis. Because it does not, there is no geokinesis in animal behaviour.

Another example of the difference has been given by Fraenkel and Gunn, drawn from the response to contact with solid surfaces, the thigmotropism of Loeb. We must now distinguish between thigmotaxis and thigmokinesis, both of which may be operative as an animal creeps to shelter in a crevice: 'the former guides the animal during locomotion, the latter determines where it shall stop'.

This particular form of behaviour is, of course, strongly developed in most members of the cryptozoic fauna; nor is it limited to small creatures, but is conspicuous in the behaviour of scorpions. L. Berland has given us a delightful comment on this tendency: 'car cet animal a le gout des pertuis, des failles, des trous, des interstices pour s'y cacher' (for this animal has a fancy for narrow passages, cracks, holes and crevices in which to hide itself). He tells us that to make these creatures comfortable and at the same time visible to spectators, the curator of the vivarium at the Paris Museum provides them with a sheet of glass, fixed horizontally just above the floor of their cage. The scorpions creep under it and have just that contact with a solid above them that their nature seems to demand; and when so placed they do not try to avoid the light that shines on them, but seems no longer to disturb or repel them.

* * * *

Thus it comes about that we are led to form a picture of the invertebrate as a sensitive, responding, living unit in a complex system of circumstances. These circumstances, the components of its environment, are constantly changing, and the changes compel response by the animal, usually in the form of movement. As it moves its direction is largely determined by the stimuli that fall upon it, until it comes to rest in a situation with which it is in bodily equilibrium.

Russell (18) describes this widespread kind of behaviour by saying that the general tendency of the animal is 'to seek its ecological norm'. When the matter is looked at in this way it gives a reasoned and acceptable estimate of the extent and value of the mechanistic point of view. One of the most cogent objections to pure mechanism is that if the animal is considered to be a machine, it should always respond to the same stimulus in the same way, and also that all the individuals in the same niche should behave in the same way when a change in the conditions occurs.

To a recognizable extent, there is truth in this. Is it not everybody's experience that the lifting of a stone or a piece of wood in their garden reveals not one but a dozen or a score of woodlice, which had congregated there because the conditions were those of their ecological norm?

A wonderfully good example of this occurs in Wood's (24) *Natural History,* published nearly a hundred years ago: 'One day this summer, as I was bathing in the river Cray, just below a lasher, I happened to look under the cross-beam of the woodwork and there saw something which I took for a mass of black horsehair. Wondering how such a substance could get into such a situation, I went to examine it, and then found that the supposed horsehair was nothing more or less than a legion of Harvest-spiders, all gathered together, their little bodies nearly hidden by their bent legs. There must have been some thousands of creatures under the beam, all perfectly motionless'.

Often there comes, of course, an active side to this gathering, when the conditions change and all the individuals are provoked into movement at the same time. The rustic's 'rain of frogs' is one example; spiders provide another. Sometimes it happens that all the small spiders living among the grass-roots of a meadow are stirred by the warmth of the sunshine to run about, spinning as they run. Soon the whole field is covered with an irridescent carpet of silk rippling and glistening in the sunlight, the product of what Bristowe (6) has so happily named 'a smother of spiders'.

V

THE COMPLEX WORLD

WHEN investigation is made into the apparently straightforward process of growth in plants, unsuspected complexities are soon revealed. Common sense suggests that water containing nutritive salts in solution, light, warmth and air are all necessary, as of course they are; but all these things are subject to variation in natural circumstances, and it is plain enough that too much water or too great a concentration of salts and too high a temperature are all undesirable. Less likely to be foreseen are the facts, which experiment has established, that continuous light is not as efficacious as the normal alternation of light and darkness, and that a short exposure to a low temperature often acts as a stimulus to germination and growth.

When, with these facts in mind, we come to consider the more sensitive, more active, animal, we shall be prepared for greater complexities and further surprises. An animal is provided with a number of sense-organs, so that it responds to many external stimuli which have no effect on plants; and its greater metabolic rate makes its responses more conspicuous and more immediate.

Further, many of these stimuli show changes in intensity, of which at least three types can be recognized. First, the stimulus may present a steady gradient of intensity, as occurs, for example, when an animal detects the smell of a distant odorous object, and, as it approaches the source of the smell, the concentration of vapour increases proportionately. Secondly, the stimulus may be suddenly eliminated or reduced for a short space of time and then may as suddenly reappear, as when sunshine and shadows from moving leaves or branches cross and recross the animal's eyes. Thirdly, the stimulus may be subject to natural rhythms, continuously maintained. The most obvious example of this is the daily alternation of light and darkness, and it should be remembered that these changes are accompanied by simultaneous changes in the temperature and relative humidity of the air. So important are these diurnal rhythms in the conditions of the environment, so pronounced are their effects on the animals and so promising is the recent work which they have inspired, that rhythmic behaviour is treated separately below.

A high proportion of the activities of invertebrates are therefore responses to changes in the nature of the environmental circumstances; and sometimes the response is of an unexpected nature, as when a fall of temperature stimulates the millipede Blaniulus to greater activity. Since many of the environmental changes cannot be detected readily, if at all, by human beings, there arises an apparent spontaneity in an animal's behaviour which seems to have originated within.

This raises a question long familiar to philosophers. Much of our own behaviour seems to us to have a spontaneous origin within ourselves, that is to say that we do some things because we have thought about them and wish to do them. Very often the thought and the wish are direct consequences of an external event, of which we are sometimes conscious and sometimes unconscious. There are those who maintain that all human behaviour is dependent on external stimuli, even though the stimulus may never reach the mind in its undisguised, recognizable form. It is difficult to discuss the state of an animal's consciousness, so that it is better to determine first how far external changes, other than those considered in the two preceding chapters, can be interpreted as causes responsible for the behaviour of an invertebrate.

* * * *

The external changes which stir an invertebrate into action are often of much greater significance to the animal than they are to a vertebrate which experiences the same stimuli. A satisfactory exposition of this difference must play an important part in the establishing of the underlying text of this book—namely, the autonomous nature of invertebrate behaviour—so that it is essential at this point to select a representative group of familiar sources of stimuli and to show how characteristic are the responses of invertebrates and how different from the responses of human beings and other vertebrates. The examples chosen in this chapter are (a) changes in humidity, (b) vibratory disturbances, (c) chemical influences.

* * * *

Many terrestrial invertebrates are the descendants of aquatic ancestors. In leaving the water for the land they have met, among other difficulties, the risk of dessication. The constantly moist skin of the earthworm, the chitinous exoskeleton of the arthropod (Fig. 7) and the calcareous shell of the mollusc are all described in the biology books as adaptations, helping to retain water in the tissues of an animal which would seriously suffer from uninterrupted evaporation. The impression is given that creatures

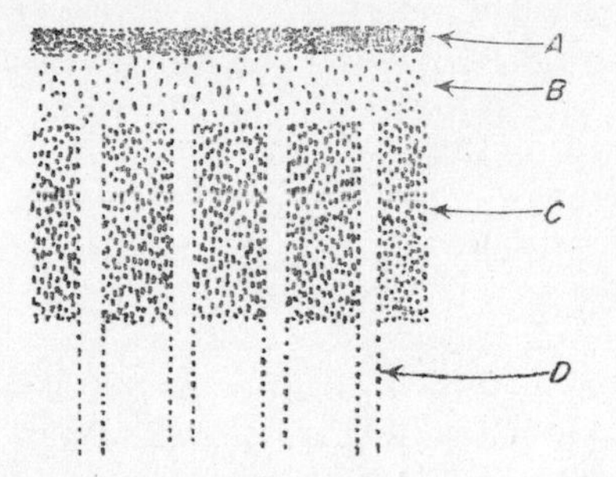

Fig. 7. Section through the epicuticle of an arthropod.
A = cement; B = wax; C = cuticulin.
These make the epicuticle, a few thousandths of a millimetre thick.
D = exocuticle of sclerotin, traversed by pore-canals.

so furnished are immune from the effects of changes in humidity.

For a long time certain exceptions to this indifference have been regarded as cases of unusual interest. For example, in the volume on Mollusca in *The Cambridge Natural History* written in 1894, A. H. Cooke (10) reported of the American genus Omalonyx that it lived habitually on vegetation overhanging water, and perished equally if placed in the liquid or removed from it. Since then it has become increasingly recognized that indifference to humidity is comparatively rare, and that chitin is not as impervious as it has been described. Among the Arachnida, harvestmen quickly die if kept in too dry a cage; and I have described how false-scorpions kept on moistened filter-paper which has begun to get dry will congregate in the areas from which the water has evaporated least.

In real scorpions, which normally live in hot, dry places, the action of the chitin is improved by a layer of wax, which has been shown by Cloudsley-Thompson (7) to retain moisture up to a temperature of 60°C.

When these responses are considered more closely they reveal an interesting and significant difference between the subject of humidity as it is treated in the textbooks of physics and as it appears in the work of the student of animal behaviour.

* * * *

The first concern of the physicist is the *absolute humidity,* a quantity simply defined as the weight of water vapour present in a cubic metre of air; but this is of less interest to many—to the meteorologist, for example—than is the *relative humidity,* or the approach of the air to saturation. This quantity, familiarly defined as the ratio between the quantity of water vapour present per cubic metre and the quantity which would be present if the air were saturated, is deducible from the readings of the wet and dry bulb thermometers, and other forms of hygroscope, and its changing value is of use in weather forecasting.

It is, however, clear enough that to an animal like a harvest-spider or a slug the really important matter is not how much water vapour the air contains, but how much more it can take up, that is to say its *saturation deficiency*. This quantity, which may be defined as the weight of water vapour necessary to saturate a cubic metre of air in the existing circumstances, is dependent on both the relative humidity and the temperature. Of course, if the relative humidity is 100% the saturation deficiency is zero whatever the temperature, but obviously air at 5°C with a relative humidity of 50% cannot absorb as much water as air also with a relative humidity of 50% but at a temperature of 50°C. The following table makes this clear enough.

It follows that to an invertebrate saturation deficiency is the condition of chief importance, rather than the familiar relative humidity; but even so the tendency to react to a given degree of

SATURATION DEFICIENCIES

TEMPERATURE	RELATIVE HUMIDITY			
	5%	25%	50%	75%
0°C	4·56 mg	3·6 mg	2·4 mg	1·2 mg
5	6·46	5·1	3·4	1·7
10	8·84	6·97	4·65	2·32
15	12·07	9·52	6·35	3·17
20	16·25	12·82	8·55	4·27
25	21·66	17·1	11·4	5·7
30	28·5	22·5	15·0	7·5
35	37·24	29·4	19·6	9·8
40	48·07	37·95	25·3	12·65

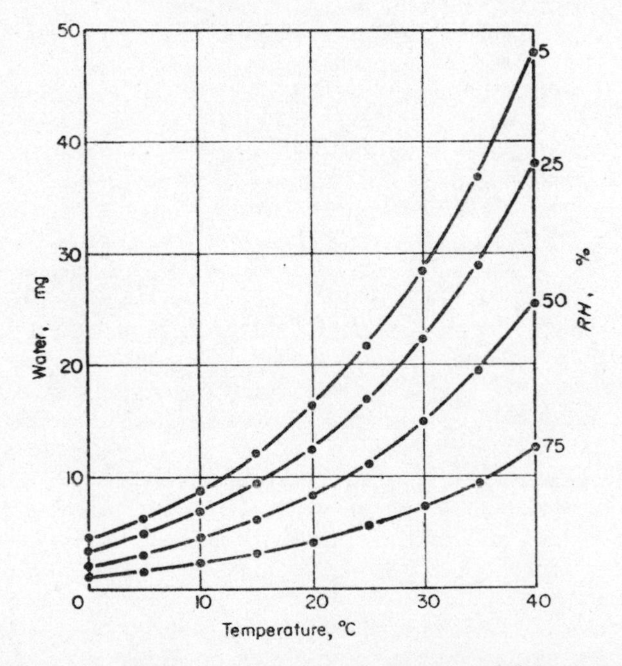

FIG. 8. Graphical representation of saturation deficiencies at different relative humidities.

saturation deficiency may be modified by the rate at which the deficiency is made up by evaporation from the tissues of the animal. In other words, it may be necessary to consider the evaporating power. Clearly perfectly dry air is not only a more effective drying agent than moist air at the same temperature, it is more effective still if it is moving, and the faster it moves the better.

This evaporating power of the air is the chief component of what is sometimes described as 'exposure', an important factor in the ecological distribution of small animals. Also, changes in evaporating power frequently act as stimuli, causing animals to leave the shelter of their resting-places or to return to them.

Few animals make their relation to water vapour plainer than do woodlice (8). Woodlice are Crustacea, which have forsaken the water in which nearly all their relatives live, and maintain a rather uncomfortable existence on land, compelled to spend nearly all their time in a moist atmosphere. In this respect they differ among themselves in a most interesting way which the British species show well. The most primitive species belong to the family Ligiidae, and are found either on the beach or, if inland, quite close to water. The family Trichoniscidae occurs only in very wet places, the Porcelliidae can live in less wet areas and the Armadilliidae are the best adapted to relatively dry air. This order is also the order of general complexity of structure, but in no family is there any device to check the loss of moisture from the body, and the differences between the families are all summarized in the length of time that they can survive in dry air.

This has a close relation to the behaviour of the animals. During the daytime they avoid light and collect in moist places. In the dark the reaction to moisture is reduced, and they can move about and feed in places where the air is drier than in their daytime shelters. Their normal photonegative tendency drives them back to hide in moist places at dawn. If, however, the moisture of their surroundings dries up, they become photopositive, and can wander about in daylight until they come upon a moist niche in which to rest until sunset. The whole forms an adequate behaviour pattern which is one of the chief adaptations of the woodlouse to a terrestrial life. There is little doubt that if other arthropods were investigated with the same precision that Drs. Edney (11) and Cloudsley-Thompson (8) have given the woodlice, similar adaptive behaviour patterns would be revealed.

* * * *

The vibratory disturbances which affect man and most other veterbrates are almost wholly confined to the vibrations of the air that constitute sound, and in most vertebrates these sound waves are received by the tympanic membrane which forms an essential part of the outer ear. The responses of invertebrates to vibrations are very different, and there is a widespread ability to detect and respond to vibrations of the ground on which the animal is standing or running.

Probably no animals show a more refined reaction to vibrations of this kind than does a web-spider, whose responses are so directed that they carry it to the insect whose struggles produce the vibrations. Strength or acuity of vision becomes of small importance; greater value attaches to the development of an exquisite sense of touch.

It is almost a surprise to find that the eyes have been retained in virtually all species. One might expect the appearance of eyeless spiders, which would have survived because in their use of their webs their blindness would not be a disadvantage. Nevertheless, this has not happened, and the phylogenist may set himself the problem of determining what advantage follows from the possession of eyes which are so subordinated to the sense of touch as are the eyes of spiders. Some selective value must lie at the back of their persistence. If, in thinking over this question, we find ourselves at the almost forgotten occupation of Victorian biologists, the game of 'Find-the-use-of', it is because the persuasiveness of the neo-Darwinians has given natural selection so exalted a position.

* * * *

The establishing of vibrotactic response as an essential component of the behaviour of web-spiders has had a number of unexpected consequences. Of these the most remarkable was the evolution of the curious type of behaviour named by its discoverer 'Netzstarrheittaxis', a directed response to the tension of the silk on which the spider was treading. This was discovered by Monika Holzapfel (14) in 1933, and it is now well known that she showed that when a spider has run across its web, and has seized its victim, its return to the corner from which it came is guided by these tensions. If they were altered by slight distortion of the box containing the web, the spider appeared to be 'lost', and, running across and across its true direction, reached home by a very devious path (Fig. 9). Of all the things that spiders do, this is perhaps the most narrowly characteristic, the furthest removed from the behaviour of all other animals. If one can imagine an acrobat who had dropped from his trapeze to the safety-net and who now, instead of looking about, plucked at the meshes with fingers and toes and so chose a path to his step-ladder, one can get some idea of what the spider does.

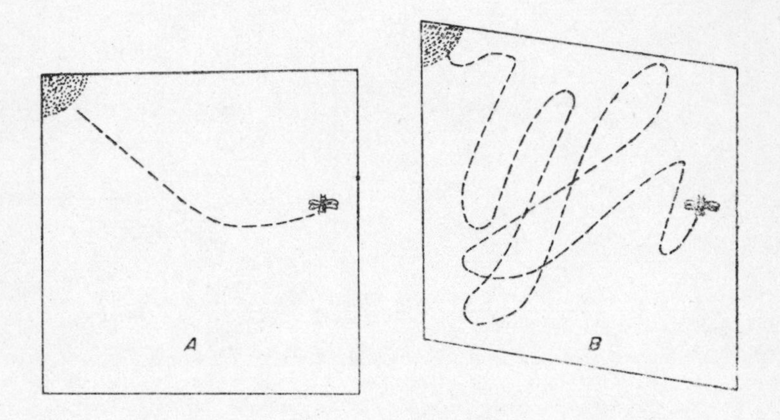

FIG. 9. Holzapfel's experiment on Netzstarrheitstaxis
A Path of spider's normal return with fly, in square cage.
B Path of spider's return in cage so distorted as to change tensions of threads.

Another consequence of the development of vibrotaxis was its use by the spider *Pirata piraticus*. This spider lives near water and hunts its prey on the surface. I have found that if it is kept in a suitable cage, which offers it a pebble beach at the water's edge, it spins itself a silk tube to live in, and stands with its forelegs resting on the surface of the liquid. In this position it closely resembles a house-spider in the tube of its web, with its forelegs resting on the sheet, so that it is no surprise to find that if one drops an insect on to the water, the spider rushes out to it and seizes it. In exactly the same way it will run out and attack a tuning-fork which lightly touches the surface. Clearly, the ripples which radiate from the centre of the disturbance guide the spider to their point of origin (Fig. 10). Here is pure vibrotaxis.

The return to the tubular web is not so easy, because the

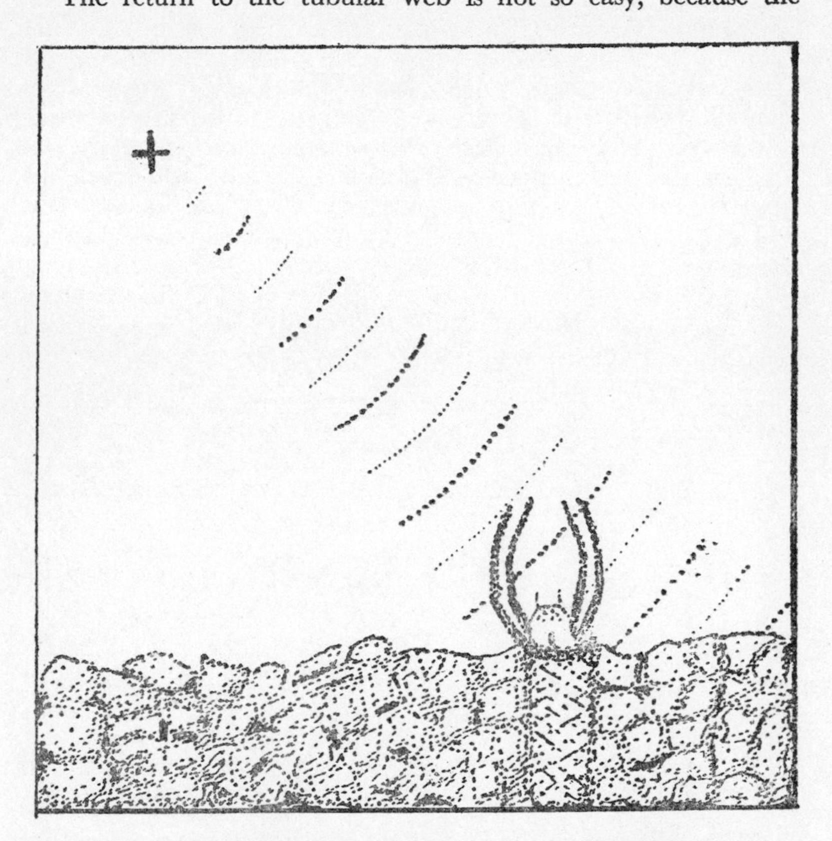

FIG. 10. Vibrotaxis in *Pirata*. The spider is directed by the ripples towards the point from which they originate.

water film cannot retain horizontal tensions and transmit them to the spider's legs. Its return may be described as an instance of mnemotaxis, which is a biologist's way of saying that the spider remembers where it has come from; but I should like to see a series of experiments with Pirata in which this point was investigated. Suppose, for example, that while the spider ran to its victim, an electric lamp was shining on its left side, and that as it seized the fly the light was switched to the other side. Whatever the result, there is no doubt that spiders accustomed to running on water possess unusual powers. P. Bonnet (5) has shown that whenever a Dolomedes was dropped into the Canal du Midi at Toulouse, it always turned so as to run to the nearer bank.

The delicacy of touch that must be necessary for this reaction is a characteristic of spiders, and suggests another investigation, which should be undertaken by some interested biologist who has the necessary equipment. All students of sound will recall the experiments on vibrating plates. A sheet of glass, supported at its centre, was thinly coated with lycopodium powder and a violin bow was then drawn across its edge at a chosen point. The form of the vibrations of the plate was made apparent by the heaping of the lycopodium in symmetrical designs, known as Chladni's figures (Fig. 11). It would be of great interest and

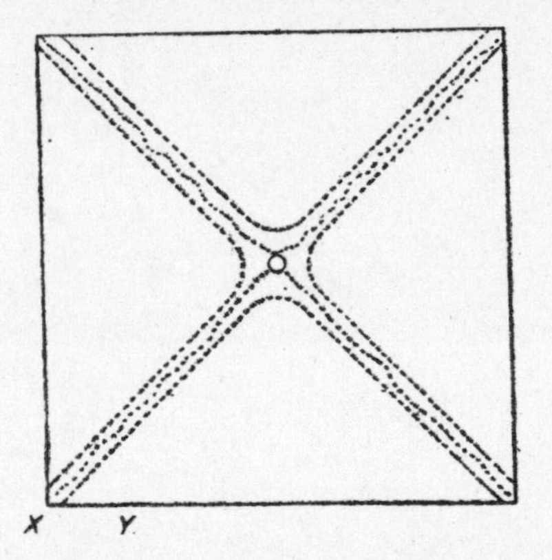

FIG. 11. Chladni's plate. The plate, fixed in the centre, is 'damped' (touched) at X and bowed at Y with a violin bow. Sand collects along the lines shown. What path would be taken by a spider, running across the vibrating plate?

significance to watch the running of a spider on a vibrating plate and to compare the path it took with these figures.

*   *   *   *

Another side of the complexity of the invertebrate's world is seen in their responses to substances which, as we should say, smell or taste conspicuously. Many reactions of insects and others to odours of many kinds have been recorded, and many instances are known in which invertebrates either limit themselves to one sort of food or show a preference for certain kinds and decisively reject others. The difference between these selective responses and those of man and other vertebrates is expressed in the word chemotactic, implying that the organ by which the stimulus is received is sensitive to contact with particular chemical substances.

Human beings cannot distinguish the flavours of their food or drink with their fingers or toes, but many invertebrates do just this. Their tarsal organs, which consist essentially of a minute depression in the surface of the exoskeleton, with a small peg-like projection at the bottom, are often easy to see, under the microscope, on the legs of spiders and other arachnids (Fig. 12). It has been shown by the experiments of Blumenthal (4) that drinking water is tested by these organs, that the animal can

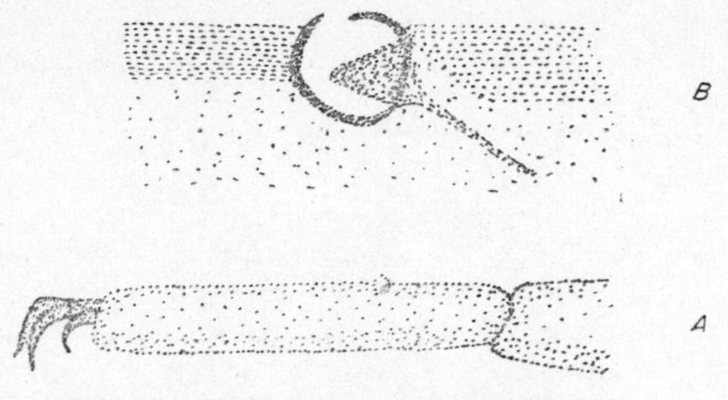

FIG. 12. The tarsal organ on a spider's leg.
A Showing the position of the organ.
B Section through simple type of organ.

distinguish water from salt or sugar solutions, and that if the organ is sealed with petroleum jelly, the reactions disappear. It has also been found that the mere touch of a nauseous insect is sufficient to make a spider reject it as food and to clean its legs after contact.

* * * *

These differences, and others, between the behaviour of vertebrates and invertebrates, find their most striking expression in the rhythms of activity which so many invertebrates show, and in the much more surprising fact that these rhythms may become so impressed on the animals that they persist in the absence of the instigating stimulus.

Obviously the most probable kind of rhythm which an animal is likely to show is a daily one. Every evening at sunset there is a fall in the intensity of the light, to which phototactic invertebrates will respond. There is also a fall in temperature, which may in itself act as a stimulus to movement, as in the millipede Blaniulus, but which also produces a rise in the relative humidity and a consequent fall in the evaporating power of the air. These may act as signals for a resumption of the business of living by many invertebrates which are customarily described as nocturnal.

That the night is a time of intense activity in the invertebrate world has only of recent years been fully realized; and there are certain fairly obvious advantages about night life which these animals have exploited. The reduction in the loss of water from the tissues is only one of these; at night enemies are more easily avoided and food is more easily obtained, so that the habit of nightly activity alternating with daily rest and concealment is easy to understand.

A fundamental peculiarity of diurnal rhythms is the existence of two kinds of rhythm, known as exogenous and endogenous. The former are direct responses to rhythmic stimuli, and do not occur if the stimulus is missing. Endogenous rhythms do not disappear, but persist for varying lengths of time, in constant conditions. As long ago as 1930 it was discovered that the organisms of the marine plankton, which rise to the surface during the day and sink below at night, will continue to rise and fall when confined in a sea-water tank kept in perpetual light.

Whereas exogenous rhythms are determined by environmental changes, endogenous rhythms are correlated with such changes, but are not direct responses to them. This is proved by the way in which a resumption of activity may often be found to begin as much as three hours before sunset. Even when the animals are in captivity, and day and night are replaced by the switching of an electric light on or off, the restlessness may be found regularly to anticipate the turning of the switch.

To detect this kind of behaviour it is necessary to devise means whereby the animal can be kept in conditions of constant temperature, light and humidity, and also to arrange the recording of its movements. This may be done by keeping it in a box which is balanced about a horizontal axis. Each time that the animal passes across the axis the box tilts and a pointer touching a revolving cylinder of smoked paper records the fact. This reveals the number of crossings in each hour of the twenty-four. The apparatus is known as an aktograph (Fig. 13).

Cockroaches, woodlice and spiders have proved themselves to be good subjects for investigations of this kind. Everyone knows that 'black beetles' come out at night, and Cloudsley-Thompson (9) has shown that a natural twelve-hour rhythm exists in the cockroach, so that when kept in constant conditions it retains the habit of increased activity in the dark.

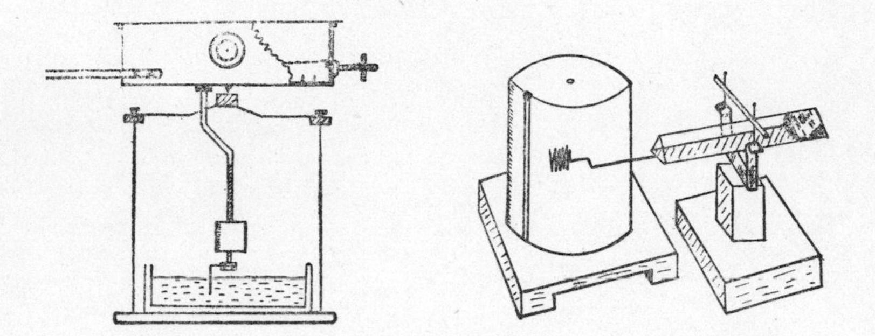

FIG. 13. An aktograph. Two types of aktograph apparatus suitable for use with millipedes and other small animals, each consisting of an arena or box pivoted on a knife-edge along its median traverse axis. Any movement of an animal along the longitudinal axis tips the arena and is recorded by a lever balanced by an adjustable counterpoise and writing on a revolving smoked drum. (After Gunn and Kennedy, 1937, and D'Aguillar, 1952.)

It is possible to modify this and to replace it by an unnatural rhythm. Thus instead of twelve hours of light alternating with twelve hours darkness, the insects may be subjected to an eight-hour cycle. After a sufficient period an eight-hour rhythm is established and is retained in constant conditions. Even such an unlikely rhythm as twenty-one hours of light and three hours of darkness can be impressed upon them.

VI

THE ANIMAL MACHINE

THE RESPONSES of animals to external stimuli, which are known as reflexes or reflex actions, the turnings of animals under unilateral or asymmetrical stimuli, which are known as tropisms, and the movements of animals under the guidance of such stimuli, which are known as taxes or kineses, all bear a certain relationship to each other. They are inborn or inherited in a way that makes them inevitable, invariable in all members of a species, and predictable, or very nearly so, by any observer who has studied the species in question and has rightly interpreted the nature of the stimulus. This constancy of behaviour among all the individuals of a species, and to some extent among related species and genera, is a phenomenon which the student of animal behaviour is required to explain. Why, for example, does a wolf-spider in Britain carry her cocoon attached to her spinnerets, and subsequently carry her young on her back, in a manner which is paralleled only by other wolf-spiders, whether they live in Australia, America or Africa.

A question similar to this was familiar years ago to the chemists who discovered, and had to convince their critics, that the salt, the chalk and the soda of Britain were exactly the same compounds as the salt, chalk and soda of Bohemia, Brazil and Borneo; and today chemists recognize the fact of constant composition. But mineral salts are not systems of the same degree of organization as animals; in animals we are perhaps uncritically inclined to look for individuality, for freedom of choice, for personal preferences, for differences in skill and achievement. When we do not find these qualities we ask, too, for an explanation of the uniformity.

From these premises a mechanistic hypothesis may easily arise. If from an animal we remove the chief origin of behaviour-differences among men, namely the mind, we are left with a co-ordinated group of systems of organs in which there can be no alternatives to machine-like responses. This is equivalent to comparing the actions of an animal to the actions of a machine, which always does the same things when set to work by its human operator, and must, inevitably, plough the earth or print a page or make a tin box according to its nature and not according to its inclinations, which are non-existent.

The simple, not to say the crude idea that an animal is no more than a machine must appear superficially unacceptable to the ordinary naturalist, who looks upon it as evidence of an exaggerated respect for the experimental methods characteristic of the physical sciences. It is therefore more than worth while to enquire into the possible causes which have contributed to the long if chequered career of this hypothesis.

One of these is certainly its inherent simplicity as a useful description or explanation of animal behaviour. There seems to be a universal desire among men to seek for simple explanations of phenomena which are not in themselves simple, and which therefore cannot possibly be expressed in simple terms. A simple explanation of animal behaviour is as impossible as a simple explanation of science itself. There are many little books in existence which profess to introduce the young reader to 'simple science', and an examination of many of them only too often suggests that the simplicity has eliminated the science, leaving nothing but the answers to the normal questions of inquisitive children. It would be unprofitable to allow the study of animal behaviour to approach this limit.

A different aspect of this desire for simplicity is seen in the tendency to stretch an accepted hypothesis or an established principle beyond the boundaries of its usefulness. The hypothesis of the reflex arc was a sound one, but when it is stretched, under the name of a chain reflex, to cover a long series of consecutive acts it begins to lose its appeal. The famous conditioned reflexes of Pavlov were impressed to an extended service, so that in his view all the actions of all animals, and even of men, were described as conditioned reflexes. A tethered animal might resist the unnatural restraint, and its resistance would be described as an instance of the freedom reflex; or a man might devote his life to the acquisition of books or of china or of pictures, not because he wanted or appreciated these things, but because of the operation of a collecting reflex.

In the same manner, Loeb attempted to describe all behaviour in terms of 'tropisms'. Principles which he and his colleagues had deduced from their experiments with small invertebrates were extended to cover the doings of men who, whether they were writing books, drinking cider or making love, were said to be performing tropistic actions.

All these are examples of a mode of thought which is common enough in everyday life, and which also appears in biological theory, where it produces misleading conclusions, misdirected efforts and mistaken hypotheses. It may be described as the synechdochaic fallacy, a substitution of the part for whole, or, in simpler words, as 'the error of nothing-but'. Familiar examples are numerous: profits are a part of business, therefore business is nothing but profit-making: physical attraction exists in love, therefore love is nothing but physical attraction: and so on. In biology this sterile type of argument is too easily accepted, chiefly because there is no general and recognized theory with which to expel it. Hence Loeb, for example, may say that all behaviour is nothing but 'tropisms', and when his critics laugh and ask whether churchgoing is 'positive theotropism', he gravely nods his assent. Darwin put forward the idea of natural selection, and as a result his followers argue as if all evolution is nothing but natural selection and that other factors must be excluded; and lastly, a physiologist detects in lungs or stomach changes of an ordinary and familiar nature, and from this, and similar details, springs the conception that life is nothing but physics and chemistry. The whole of the mechanistic theory in biology is founded on this synechdocaic fallacy.

In addition to these reasons for supporting mechanistic theories, there may be mentioned the interesting achievements of the instrument-makers, who long ago produced a contraption known as the 'heliotropic dog'. This was propelled by a motor which worked in connection with two 'eyes', which were really selenium cells. These effected the steering of the dog, because the conductivity of selenium is proportional to the intensity of the light falling on it. The dog automatically follows a light; or, by a simple reversal of its mechanism, avoids it. The accomplishments of this toy are primitive when compared with the far more elaborate behaviour of the robot 'tortoises' beloved of the students of cybernetics. This new word, derived from the Greek *kubernao,* I steer, is the name of the science of governing mechanisms, or the study of the process rather than the actual structure of the machine.

When we are told how robot-tortoises move about, how they react when they meet each other, how they return to their homes for recharging when their motive power is failing, and how they can learn to find their way through mazes, we are tempted, for a moment, to believe that the dividing line between the organism and the machine is finer than we had thought. Next we remember that calculating machines today are described by their makers as having memories, and that there are machines which can translate Chinese into Russian; and we are almost convinced that the line does not exist.

Yet, after all, and surprising or even fantastic as are the apparent powers of these indubitably remarkable pieces of mechanism, it remains true that no one has been able to demonstrate that their performances have helped us towards an understanding of any of the difficulties which the study of animal behaviour raises; nor, perhaps, were they primarily intended to do so.

* * * *

It is unfortunately true that mechanism as a general biological hypothesis is very definitely a hypothesis that is attractive to the less experienced scientist. In this it is not unique: there are other doctrines whose appeal is chiefly to the immature. For example, it has been said that 'if you are not a Socialist before you are thirty, you have no heart; and if you are a Socialist after you are thirty, you have no head'. With the truth or falsity of this antithesis a biologist is fortunately unconcerned; but a closely parallel form of statement may as usefully be made, as follows: 'If you are not a mechanist before you are thirty, you know no science; if you are a mechanist after you are thirty you know no biology'.

For the mechanistic hypothesis, whatever its value may be, always fails, sooner or later, to carry conviction. Animals often behave as if they were machines, and whenever they do so the mechanist is safe in using them as the subjects of his experiments. Mechanism is perfectly sound as the laboratory hypothesis of the biochemist.

But though sound in the biochemical laboratory, it fails in logic, and so cannot commend itself for universal acceptance. Joad (15), following McTaggart, demolished the mechanistic doctrine with the following argument. 'If materialism is correct, the mind is part of (or a function of) the brain. Our thoughts then reflect—in the last resort they *are*—movements in the brain, and they are determined therefore by these movements. We think our thoughts, not because they are true, but because our brain passes through certain cerebral states. Truth, in fact, on this view is an inadmissible concept, since the notion of truth involves the idea that an idea can be tested by something other than its relation to the brain—something which can convict it, for example, of being either true or erroneous. Now, if materialism is right, our thoughts can—indeed, they must—be chemically sound, since they must reflect the workings of our brain; but they cannot be logically sound. To say of a materialist's thought that it is logically correct would be like affirming of a gland or a nerve-cell that it was logically correct. Hence, if materialism is right, our thoughts cannot be true. Now, the theory of materialism is itself a structure of thought; consequently it follows that what it asserts cannot be true. Hence materialism is not true'.

If this argument is accepted as impeccable logic—and it is difficult to see how it can be rejected—the materialistic point of view, and all that follows from it, like mechanism in biology, must be abandoned.

A comparable and perhaps a rather simpler way of expressing the same idea is as follows. The mechanistic biologist looks upon the animal he is studying, be it earthworm, barnacle, blow-fly larva or sea-anemone, as a machine. He tries, as we have seen, to spread his mechanistic ideas down to the protozoa and up to the mammals, until he has convinced himself that, at all levels, an animal is a machine. He cannot therefore decline to take the last step, namely that man, one of the mammals, is also a machine. This has brought him to the necessity of supporting the doctrine that man is a machine which holds a belief that it is a machine. With such a conclusion neither biology, nor science in general, nor common sense can do anything.

A possible alternative leads similarly to an impasse. Grant me, says the mechanist, that my barnacle larva is purely mechanical, and I, in return, will grant that you and some other animals possess purposive minds. This compromise, which seems so hopeful, implies a division of the animal kingdom into mindless automata and minded intelligentia, and so at once provokes the question, 'Where do you draw the dividing line?'. This question has been asked for many generations, but has never yet received a satisfying answer.

Mechanism cannot be dismissed without a glance at its methodological aspect, already mentioned briefly in Chapter I. It was there suggested that instead of supporting the uncompromising Cartesian statement, 'Animals are mere machines', a student of animal behaviour should subscribe to a more cautious opinion and should suggest instead that animals may be usefully studied as if they were machines.

An important reason for adopting this view is, first, that it saves the biologist from committing himself in advance to a definite opinion about the phenomena he is going to study: in place of a dogmatic assertion about animals it foreshadows a method of investigation. Further, there is the advantage that it opens the door to the experimental method, which is a characteristic of science and at the same time banishes any undue sense of wonder and mystery.

The contrast between these two approaches to the difficulties in the interpretation of animal behaviour can be made clearer by a consideration of an analogous problem in the science of chemistry.

When John Dalton published his Atomic Hypothesis in 1805 his statesments included among other things: (i) all elements are made of indivisible atoms, (ii) all the atoms of one element are the same in properties and weight. These statements were made because they were apparently logical deductions from the results of gravimetric experiments, and for a long time they were accepted as being expressions of the truth. It is to be observed that they take the form of dogmatic assertions of fact about the nature of the elements and the nature of atoms, and in consequence they can be described as ontological atomism.

The discovery of the electron by J. J. Thomson and of isotopes by F. S. Soddy showed that both these statements were untrue, and that Dalton had made from the experimental data deductions which were unjustifiable and indeed unjustified. What might he have said? Clearly he might more cautiously have postulated: elements react (i) as if they were made of indivisible atoms, and (ii) as if all the atoms of an element have the same average weight'. If he had written thus he would have produced an hypothesis which could have been described as methodological atomism. It would have confined itself to a possible interpretation of the gravimetric laws of chemistry and it would have avoided direct statements about the constitution of matter.

Chemists, in fact, might well have said, 'As to whether the elements are composed of indivisible atoms, or not, we have no direct knowledge, but experiment shows that they react as if they are'.

Further, this more cautious wording would in no way have impaired the usefulness of Dalton's atomic hypothesis as a guiding principle, in the light of which chemists might work and interpret their results. It was fortunate for the progress of chemistry that, in their uncompromising form, Dalton's statements were no hindrance, but were a stimulus and a help. The progress was such that in due time the original form of the hypothesis was shown to be unacceptable.

This recalls the method of dialectics, a species of logical argument which, starting from an original statement, continues until the progress made reveals that statement as untrue. Dalton's atomic hypothesis may be said to have been so good that it led to its own disproof.

* * * *

When these ideas are applied to the study of animal behaviour, the position which may be recommended is obvious enough. To say unhesitatingly that animals are mere machines is to make a statement about the nature of living organisms which, even if it had been deduced from observations of behaviour under experimental conditions, is unjustifiable. If it is adopted and followed, it leads, and leads very quickly, to its own disproof, and the ontological mechanist has stranded himself in an unenviable position.

The alternative form of statement may be made thus: as to whether organisms are, or are not, machines we have no knowledge; we do not yet know the nature of life, the nature of mind nor the nature of the relation between the mind and the body; but experience suggests that animals may usefully be studied, adopting the methods of the physical sciences, as if they were machines. Thus guarded, the position is unassailable: it remains only to determine whether it is worth defending.

And of course it is. When animals are experimentally treated as if they were automata, when the speeds of their movements are measured, when the angles through which they turn themselves are observed, when the proportions of a group which congregate in the wet, the damp and the dry parts of a graded atmosphere are counted, when all these things, and many others, are done, valuable knowledge about the ways of living creatures is acquired. Our results can be expressed in a vocabulary which is more acceptable than an uncritical statement about an animal's dislikes or wishes. Some of the more surprising things that animals do begin to be a little less incomprehensible. We have made biological progress.

* * * *

There is a stretch of no-man's-land where the two sides of mechanism face each other at no great distance, and where the question which both are trying to answer is the same. This is simply, How far is mechanism a helpful idea, giving a true picture of an organism without introducing a suspicion of caricature? And the first answer is that it depends on the organism.

In the biology of plants mechanism is almost wholly adequate. The so-called behaviour of plants, which consists of morphogenetic growth and the various tropistic movements of their roots, leaves and other parts, seem to be nothing more than direct response to the nature of the environment. No one seriously suggests that in these movements a plant gives any evidence of knowing, feeling or striving; it is only showing us the results of that power of response to external stimuli which is a characteristic of all living things. A plant is therefore the mechanist's ideal organism; it fits the old description, 'a more or less constant form of a flow of particles', so completely that no botanist suggests an alternative view, and in botany there is no perceptible controversy between mechanism and vitalism.

At the other end of the scale, represented by the biology of man, and in fact represented no less efficiently by the higher animals, mechanism is as wholly unacceptable. A man is not a machine, and his dog is not a machine, and no amount of argument, or introduction of protective words like 'as if', will make them so.

Between these two extremes lies the whole of the animal kingdom with its wide variation of structure and organization. It is clear enough that although mechanism must give a caricature of a bird or a mammal it can be made to give a picture of a crayfish or a snail which may be described as reasonably good; and, further, that the mechanistic picture of a sponge or a protozoon may appear to be even closer to the real life of the animal. The question which the mechanist may legitimately ask, whether he be physiologist, ecologist or student of behaviour, is therefore, How far can the biology of this or that organism be satisfactorily described in the essentially quantitative, experimental language of chemistry and physics; and where does the imponderable, whether it be called mind or psyche or entelechy or life itself, appear and make ordinary physics and chemistry inadequate?

VII

THE INSTINCTIVE LEVEL

In his lively autobiography, *All the Days of My Life,* S. P. B. Mais has written the following dramatic paragraph, which has a very considerable biological interest: 'I went into a nursing home on 24 July 1914 and died the following morning under an operation which lasted two hours. I only learned of my death twenty-two years later. How long my heart stopped beating I do not know—was it twenty minutes?—but it was long enough for the surgeon to have given me up when my heart began to beat again as suddenly and unexpectedly as it had stopped'.

It appears that in saying that he died on the morning of 25 July, Mais was making use of an author's licence; it is equally clear that during the interval in which his heart was not beating he, Mais, was not alive in any ordinary sense of the word. On the other hand it seems also to be true that the cells and tissues of his body had not undergone that permanent and irreversible change known as death; they were, individually, alive in a way that Mais himself was not. When his heart began to beat again, the lives of all these cells resumed co-ordination and there emerged the life of a man.

Other examples exist to show that the principle involved is a general one. Many a child enters the world in a closely comparable condition, a condition in which the balance may be tilted either way, according to treatment. Neglected, the infant may quickly pass beyond the possibility of succour, and will be described as still-born; but given hopeful attenion, in the form, perhaps, of a smack on the back, it may come to life, take its first breath and utter its first cry.

In both these examples it is clear that a distinction can be drawn between the life of the organism and the life of the cells and tissues; to put it briefly, in the putative corpse the cells are alive but they do not act in co-ordination.

The record of Mais's unusual experience illustrates very clearly the fact that the word 'life' has several meanings, which can be and should be distinguished. The ordinary biology book does not attempt this, but includes them all in one inexplicable mystery;

yet clearly there exist living matter, the living cell, the living organism and the living community.

In this short series the widest gap occurs between the second and third terms A living cell operates under more or less constant conditions; for example the muscle cells of the human biceps and the nerve cells of the human fingers are not subjected to much variation. Indeed, a large part of the processes of animal physiology tends to keep the internal environment constant within very narrow limits. But an organism lives in a constantly changing environment, and, as has been shown, survives only because it as constantly responds to external change. This continuing reaction between organism and environment is what organismal life *is*.

The forms of behaviour with which the previous chapters have dealt, reflexes, tropisms, taxes and to some extent kineses, are all forms of behaviour which take place because the cells are alive: the forms of behaviour which remain to be considered are forms which occur because the organism is alive and is *en rapport* with its complex environment.

Although in almost all examples of classification, the steps tend to grade into each other, it is for the moment helpful to emphasise the distinction which we have tried to indicate:

Behaviour of the reflex type is the outward sign of the life of the cells. It is a response to external stimuli and restores the equilibrium between the organs and systems within the animal's body. It can be usefully examined on mechanistic principles, since it is mainly concerned with attaining a result, and no conscious control need be postulated in describing it.

Behaviour of the instinctive type is the outward sign of the life of the organism. It is a response to the situation and restores the equilibrium between the animal and the external environment. It cannot be satisfactorily treated on mechanistic principles, since it is mainly concerned with achieving a purpose, and a degree of conscious control appears to accompany it.

This comparison brings us, none too soon, to the necessity of discussing the meaning of the word instinct. The older view, common at the beginning of the present century, was a very definite one and was in part a reaction against the even older tendency to use the word as if it were in itself an explanation of behaviour. There is no such thing as instinct, we were told by Lloyd Morgan and his school, it is wiser never to use the word, but to speak only of instinctive behaviour. But Bierens de Haan (3) the well-known animal psychologist, will have none of this. His view is that 'instinct is the innate psychological structure which couples a special affection to a special cognition and a special conation to a special affection, and on the other hand couples a special cognition and an affection to a special conation'.

The jargon in which this definition is stated (or perhaps into which it has been translated) does not make it conspicuously easy to understand. Its implication appears to be that instinct supplies the necessary union between stimulus, from without or within or both, and the initiation of the appropriate type of response.

Bierens de Haan helps us out of this unpromising position by telling us that instinct is a purely psychological phenomenon, and as such can only be described in psychological terms, producing a psychologist's definition, like the one quoted above. The instinctive action, however, is a biological phenomenon, to be defined in terms of biology. The biologist's task, therefore, is to choose acceptable terms, which will express the chief characteristics of instinctive actions. In view of the fact that biologists are looking at the instinctive actions of animals during a large part of their work, this ought not to be difficult; so that we can immediately state, briefly, the five features of all behaviour that can properly be called instinctive.

(i) It is born in, or inherited by, the animal, and therefore does not have to be learnt.

(ii) It is perfectly or at least adequately carried out on the occasion of its first performance, and therefore does not have to be practised.

(iii) It appears in response to a definite situation, in which stimuli from both outside and inside the animal are concerned.

(iv) It is performed without necessary knowledge of the relation between the actual movements or operations and the end to which the behaviour must ultimately lead.

(v) It is carried through continuously with scant regard for changed conditions or abnormal circumstances, and is only exceptionally liable to modification by unusual circumstances or by experience.

No useful purpose would be served by attempting to compress all these qualities of instinctive behaviour into a few terse phrases, such as by convention constitute a definition, but they are all so important that each of them deserves separate consideration.

* * * *

1. To say that instinctive behaviour is inborn appears to be as axiomatic as to say that reflex behaviour is inborn. In general terms this is true, but there is a word of caution to be added. There are forms of behaviour which are not learned, but which are not wholly inherited or 'genetically determined', as they are now sometimes described. The most familiar example is the behaviour of the queen bee, when compared with that of the worker bee, a difference which covers almost every aspect of the lives of these two kinds of females. Yet it is ultimately determined by the type of food, 'royal jelly', on which the larva has been fed; in other words the innate behaviour is in part a product of the environment.

Behaviour which is wholly inherited ought to be independent of the environmental conditions. Such behaviour should suffice for survival in an environment which was quite unvarying, but no such environment exists in nature. A few essentials, such as the presence of water, may be constant or nearly so, but for the rest the organism is bound to acquire experience of the normal and frequently rhythmical changes in its environmental conditions, and these must inevitably make a contribution towards the establishment of its normal behaviour pattern. Ordinarily these experiences will be shared by all members of a species, who will ordinarily react in the same way, 'acquire the same habits' and so produce a final behaviour-pattern which will seem to be a characteristic of the species, i.e., to be 'species-predictable'.

This means that in animals, as in man, all normal behaviour is a mixture of learned and unlearned elements; that environment and heredity have both taken a share in producing the successfully surviving organism. It also suggests the possibility of interesting results from a series of experiments designed to compare the behaviour shown in different environments by animals of the same genetic constitution with the behaviour shown in the same environment by animals of different genetic constitutions.

2. Perfect or adequate performance of complex operations on the occasion of their first necessity is a feature of instinctive actions which is divisible into two groups. The first group includes those actions which the animal must perform throughout its life,

from early youth onwards; the second group contains the actions that are confined to mature creatures only. These are dealt with in the next section, where they properly belong.

There is no better example of an instinctive action of a young invertebrate than the very familiar one of the spinning of the spider's web. The orb-web in particular is complex enough to make imperfect or simplified designs at least possible in extreme youth, and yet the first and early webs of young spiders differ from those of their elders only in actual size and in matters of detail. There is no difference in essential principles : the operation in all its complexity is potentially possible from the very first.

Moreover, it would be surprising if juvenile webs were describable as imperfect or simple, if such a description implied that they were less efficient than the webs of their parents. An organism, may it be emphasised at the risk of repetition, is extremely vulnerable, and its life is so precarious that any inefficiency of the type common in human beings and human institutions is quickly followed by extinction. It is thus unlikely that spiderlings, even though they start with the advantage of a stomachful of yolk, would stand any chance of catching enough food if their webs were actually inefficient. It is much more probable that their small and delicate webs are adapted to entangle the particular kinds of small insects which the young spider is able to overcome.

3. An instinctive action does not in general appear unless circumstances make it desirable, which implies that a stimulus is a first necessity. This of course is true of reflex actions also, and a distinction between the two may be found in the simplicity of the stimulus in one case and its relative complexity in the other. The opening and closing of the iris, for example, is a response to a change in the intensity of illumination, and nothing else is needed to induce it. Instinctive actions are more likely to appear in response to a combination of stimuli, so that a stimulus-situation is built up, and the consequences inevitably follow.

Among the many activities of many animals which may be looked on in this way, few can be better than the curious actions which often precede mating and which are called courtship. The first point that is obvious about invertebrate courtship is that it appears only when the animal is sexually mature. Immature individuals have never been seen to perform any of these antics, even in a rudimentary form, and equally no mature one seems to be incapable of them. This implies that whatever the external stimulus may be it is impotent and produces no response unless it is supplemented by the effect of hormones from the glands within.

The nature of the external stimulus is extremely well shown by the thorough work of B. J. Kaston (16) on wolf-spiders and especially on the species *Pardosa milvina* (Fig. 14). He found that males of this species began to court if they were touched with a recently autotomized leg of a female, held by the experimenter in forceps. It was then found that the leg of a male had no effect

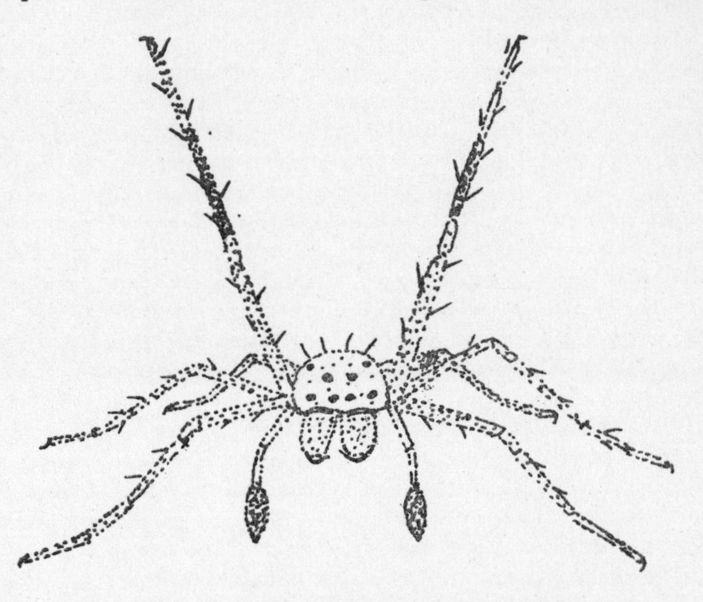

FIG. 14. Courtship attitude of *Pardosa milvina.*

when it was used in the same way. This suggested that the female legs produced a substance, which the male legs did not, to which a male was sensitive by chemo-reception. A series of experiments were then carried out in which female legs were thoroughly washed in ether and then used to touch the males. It was found that they produced no reaction.

Next, the ether was allowed to evaporate on a glass plate over which male spiders were induced to walk. It produced no effects. But if, while they were standing on the plate, they were touched with an ether-washed leg, courtship began at once. The general conclusion, which was confirmed by observations on other spiders belonging to other families, is that the appearance of these typically instinctive actions is a response to the stimulus-situation made up of gonadial maturity, tactile sensations from the female leg and chemo-reception of an ether-soluble substance usually present on the leg.

4. One of the most conspicuous differences between reflex and instinctive actions is that the former are concerned with affairs of the moment only, while the latter are not.

We are accustomed to say that the hunting wasp lays its eggs in a paralysed caterpillar, which provides the larva, when hatched, with a supply of fresh protein. We wonder at the ability of the wasp so to sting the caterpillar as to paralyse it without killing it; but we are usually careful not to say that the wasp stings the caterpillar in order to provide its offspring with food. In other words, we cannot accept the idea that the wasp conceives a purpose which will be achieved in the distant future and adapts its behaviour towards its fulfilment.

On the other hand, the wasp's actions, finding the caterpillar, carrying it to the cell, paralysing it, depositing an egg and sealing the cell, cannot be interpreted at all, that is to say they cannot be said to make sense, unless the whole story is borne in mind.

This feature of the instinctive behaviour of animals therefore brings emphatically into the foreground the large and important question of purposes. In so far as the problem of animal behaviour is a problem of interpretation, it is almost wholly a problem of discussing this formidable word, purpose.

In part the difficulty is, again, a failure of language to provide sufficient distinctive terms for different ideas, so that there are too many unrelated kinds of 'purposes' in our everyday conversations. The position can be made easier to understand by considering a series of these conversational 'purposes'.

(a) Men are usually conscious of their purposes, and are prepared to explain and to try to justify them, even when they have done the more surprising things that earn them short paragraphs in the evening newspapers. Further, a man may carry out an action, or a prolonged course of actions, with the intention of attaining a result in the distant future. Thus the intentions of a man may be indicated by his foresight or by his restraint, as when he denies himself a wife because of some peculiarity of civilization; or as when a hungry polar explorer limits himself to thirty ounces of food a day in order that he may attain a result at the end of a long and difficult journey, whereas his sledge-dog, if it finds an opportunity of breaking into the biscuit tank, shows no restraint at all.

(b) A spider spins a web; as a result it catches flies for food which without the web it would never secure. It seems to be logical to say that the obtaining of food was the purpose for which the web was spun, for so it appears to us and we can think of no other reason for web-making. But we do not know whether the spider was conscious of this purpose, though we strongly suspect that it was not. We may or may not believe that it was conscious of the act of spinning. In consequence of this ignorance of the spider's motives, we may think it wiser to describe the event more objectively, to say that the biological significance of web-spinning is that it provides the spinner with food. And when we ask the fundamental question, Why does the spider spin a web? we can find one way of answering by referring to the function of the web. This may not satisfy every questioner, and there may be other ways.

(c) My alimentary canal, with its secretions and its peristaltic actions, is digesting my breakfast. The result is the passing of nourishment to the cells and tissues of my body. I am quite sure that my alimentary tract is not conscious of any purpose in its actions, and these actions can never be ascribed to anything except the canal's functions.

(d) A machine makes a tin box. There is no question of its being conscious, but it is true to say that it is fulfilling the purpose of its owner or maker or operator or all three. It is difficult to think of a machine that works without a purpose; but it is a purpose conceived by a man and the machine's concern is only with the result.

(e) Rain containing dissolved carbon dioxide acts on a chalk cliff in which there are caves: the result is the formation of stalactites, perhaps beautiful or colourful or weird. Here there is no purpose conceivable or describable, and an answer to the question Why do the stalactites appear? can be given only in terms of a chemical process, involving the production and decomposition of calcium bicarbonate. Even if we assume that the Universe has a purpose (incomprehensible to human minds) and that the Earth has a part to play in this purpose, it is scarcely conceivable that the formation of stalactites in caves can be involved in it.

A review of the five terms of this series shows that the crux of the whole business is this. The man is fully aware of his intentions; but the spider can be no more than faintly aware of what it is doing at the moment. There is a similarity between the action of the spider and the action of the intestine, which is expressed by saying that both are performing a necessary function. In the last two cases there is no inherent purpose at all.

One of the most patient and enthusiastic students of animal behaviour, the late Sir Arthur Thomson of Aberdeen, used to say of instinctive actions that they were accompanied by a feeble endeavour and a faint awareness. Within its limits this is a satisfying position to adopt, but it pre-supposes the existence of an animal mind to express the endeavour and to experience the awareness; or otherwise there is no difference between the making of the web (b) and the making of the tin box (d). Thomson's point of view is supported by E. S. Russell's (18) opinion that 'purely instinctive, absolutely unintelligent behaviour is probably a myth'.

5. A very familiar comment on instinct is that it drives the animal through an invariable routine and forces it to carry out its activities with no regard for changes in the circumstances.

It may be noted, first, that a fixity of instinct is wholly consistent with the idea expressed above of the primitive nature of the awareness and the endeavour behind the behaviour. The two characteristics of instinct are really two views of the same feature. A parallel may help to make the matter clear. The more keenly a batsman is aware of the methods of a bowler, the effects of wind and wicket, and the placing of fieldsmen, the more variety he is able to introduce into his strokes; whereas a hitter 'pure and simple, relying on instinct' cannot do this, and the influence of the two types of batsmanship on survival is closely akin to the survival of an animal.

Secondly, it is significant to notice that while many instinctive actions have been seen to occur in modified forms as a result of experience or under experimental conditions, all instinctive actions are not equally malleable. It is apparent that instinctive urges are strongest in matters of sex, that is to say that sexual behaviour is least subject to variation and shows least plasticity.

Hence sex behaviour is the best example in which to study instinct from the point of view of its constancy. The instinctive behaviour that deals with less vital operations is less rigid. The law is that there is an inverse variation between the importance of the action for the race and the plasticity of the instinct. Actions more important for the individual are more subject to modification under pressure from the environment. It is as though the care for the race could not permit the vagaries or idiosyncrasies of the individual to threaten the fundamental business of multiplication.

* * * *

Many writers have laid emphasis on the so-called failures of instinctive behaviour, and have thought, I believe erroneously, that the recording of such failures can teach us something about the role of instinct in the life of the animal. There are several reasons for which I do not think that this can be so.

Most important is the fact that a high proportion of these so-called failures have occurred in laboratories, in circumstances which the animal would never be likely to meet in nature. Nature seldom plays tricks: she does not move captured caterpillars away from a wasp's cell, does not extract the eggs from a half-finished cocoon, does not lead processionary caterpillars on to the rim of a flower-pot. It is of little value for us to do these things, or others like them, because the behaviour of an animal, no less than its structure, is adapted to its environment, and its capabilities are adapted to the circumstances which that environment normally provides.

Again, enthusiastic students of the paralysing wasps have sometimes examined a number of the victims and have recorded the fact that a certain proportion of them had been unsuccessfully immobilized. Either they had been killed, so that they would have decayed by the time that the wasp larvae appeared, or they were not paralysed enough, so that they could still move and so injure either egg or grub. But no reason has ever been adduced for expecting perfect surgical skill in a female wasp. Why indeed should uniform perfection be expected of small animals when it is not to be found in intelligent human beings?

Herein lies another unjustified expectation to which students of animal behaviour often commit themselves. They write as if every individual of the same sex and species was endowed with exactly the same capacities, in sense organs, nervous system and muscles, like so many robots. There is no reason for making this assumption, which is contrary to our experience and to the accepted principle of variation. D. W. Morley (17) has told us of lazy ants and energetic ants, members of the same nest. M. Thomas (21), who has made a very large number of observations on instinctive behaviour. is emphatically of the same opinion. He writes: 'Ces facultés varient non seulement d'espèce à espèce, mais aussi d'individu à individu, tout comme on le constate entre les races humaines et les divers individus d'une même race.' (These faculties vary not only from one species to another, but also from one individual to another, just as may be seen among human races, and among different individuals of the same race.)

The same kind of criticism can be made about some of the problems which experimental biologists set before animals, expecting them to find a solution. When, for example, a cat is confined in a box from which by pulling a particular ring it can escape and reach a meal of fish awaiting it outside, the animal is in a position in which it would be most unlikely to find itself in nature. It may find the ring by chance, and may remember its discovery, so that it can use the same method again and earn the reputation of being a clever cat. But when one day it is freely offered the fish and yet unnecessarily enters the box and pulls the ring before it takes the first mouthful, it is making a much more significant criticism of the form of the experiment than any criticism which the experimenter may make of its instincts.

Invertebrates are even less favourable objects for experiments of this kind. When any invertebrate is placed in a situation which presents a problem, and achieves, perhaps, a solution, it is an *ad hoc* solution only, and is not necessarily of great value when the ultimate circumstances are considered. If *Convoluta roscoffensis* is short of food, it digests its symbiotic Chlorellae, in the absence of which it then dies. Its concern is with the immediate present; it has not the ability to look ahead.

This principle must never be forgotten when an attempt is made to interpret the most ordinary of instinctive actions. All the time we should seek to answer the question, 'What is the animal doing now?' and not the tempting alternative, 'What is going to happen in the end?' The latter is a question that betrays, and springs from, the human point of view, whereas it is the animal's point of view that we ought to try to learn. When the continuing actions have assuaged the animal's urge and the activity has ceased, we may reconstruct the whole story, but we should avoid the temptation to impute to the animal a motive or a purpose which we ourselves detect, and describe in terms of the result. As Tinbergen (23) says, 'To ascribe a causal function to something that is not objectively observable often leads to false conclusions. It is especially dangerous if the acceptance kills our urge for further research'.

That it should not be allowed to do so is emphasized by the work of Crane and Drees on jumping spiders. They found that a flat model of a female would stimulate a male to raise his fore-legs, but that only a solid model would provoke the typical dance. Further, attempts to feed were elicited by models, and the optimum size of model increased as the spider grew hungrier. These experiments showed that 'releasers', or signals for special responses, such as occur in nature, can be imitated in the laboratory and made to deceive the spider.

VIII

THE INVERTEBRATE MIND

IN ALL the realm of biology there can be few subjects so elusive, so likely to raise emphatic criticism on the part of the reader, and so difficult to discuss conclusively as the subject of the mind of an animal, whether the animal be amoeba, annelid or ape.

The word 'mind' itself raises the first problem, for it is a word that is difficult to define, and some writers wish, for this reason alone, to condemn all discussion as necessarily sterile. This opinion will not be accepted here: mind, like space and time, is one of those concepts which seem to defy description in words because of their fundamental nature; but like them it has to be used to express an idea with which everyone is really quite familiar.

This position has been taken by a well-known psychologist who wrote that the subject he was about to discuss was 'Whatever there is in animals that corresponds to the origin of thoughts in man'. The phrasing of his sentence is wholly admirable; firstly, because there will be few readers unwilling to admit that thoughts arise in their own minds; secondly, because there is no suggestion that an animal's thoughts are similar to the thoughts of man, but only that they arise from a corresponding origin; and thirdly, because of the cautious restraint of the first three words.

'Whatever there is.' This opening provides an opportunity for a sound start, because it suggests immediately two very different points of view: *either* (1) there is nothing in animals in which thoughts originate; *or* (2) there is something in animals in which thoughts originate.

These two statements are logically opposite to one another. They cannot both be true; if one of them is held to be true, then the other must be held to be false; and any evidence in favour of one of them is necessarily evidence against the other.

This is an ideal position, and happy indeed is either scientist or philosopher whose theories lead him to such a point. A parallel case may be recalled from the last century, when the nature of light was under discussion. Either, said the physicists, light consists of undulations in an all-pervading medium, or it consists of particles emitted rapidly in straight lines. It cannot be both. These scientists were particularly fortunate, because their two hypotheses led them to expect different velocities of light in glass. On one hypothesis this velocity must be greater, on the other it must be less, than the velocity in air. It could not be both, and an *experimentum crucis,* or crucial experiment, was at once indicated to decide between them.

The animal psychologist is not quite as happily placed as this, but the position outlined above is to a large extent a comparable one.

The first statement was that there is nothing in animals that corresponds to the origin of thoughts in man. If this is true, then the only possible conclusion is that of the ontological mechanist, namely that animals are machines, organic machines, complicated machines, but still nothing more than physico-chemical systems, just as plants are.

The comparison between a mechanist's animal and a plant has been made already in Chapter III, and need not be repeated here. All that is necessary is to point out that ontological mechanism is very far from compelling universal acceptance. However persuasively the biochemist may preach his doctrine, an animal does not seem to be a machine or a mechanical system; it seems to everyone who has watched it carefully, outside the austere walls of a physiological laboratory, to be much more obviously a sentient being, trying, now in one way, now in another, to attain some end. Despite the risks we run—and they have been adequately treated in the foregoing pages—in speaking of an animal's object, motive or purpose, the undoubted view of the majority is that the animal is not just a machine. It is widely accepted that no useful end is served by so regarding it; and the idea that there is nothing in animals that corresponds to the origin of thoughts in man must be rejected.

This rejection logically compels us to accept its alternative, but it will be wise to examine this closely, as far as possible without prejudging the result.

The behaviourist's attitude to the question of the animal mind is direct and uncompromising. He says, in effect, that a mind cannot be directly observed, and that observation is the only truly scientific way of obtaining knowledge, therefore we can have no knowledge about mind. This compels us to assume that it has no influence on behaviour, because the admission that it had any such influence would be a confession that we had that small amount of knowledge about it.

This complete negation of the whole matter is very closely related to the view of the ontological mechanist and, like that, it must be hejected as being unhelpful. In its place may be put the ready admission that there is an inherent difficulty in conceiving and describing the nature of the union between mind and matter which constitutes the living organism, the psychosome, but that the difficulty is one of a very peculiar kind. In order to define or explain the nature of this composite being it is necessary, as in all cases of defining or explaining, to describe the unknown in terms of the known; and we cannot do this here because in one way it was never unknown. It has always been a part of our fundamental consciousness that we ourselves are composed of body and mind, so that an especially intimate type of relativity prevents us from finding words to express the inexpressible.

But the recognition of this type of difficulty should not prevent us from attempting to deduce the nature of the working of the animal mind, and the foregoing chapters have contained material from which such deductions can be made. What are they?

1. It is almost axiomatic to suggest that the animal mind is of a simple, undeveloped type. This suggestion implies that in an entity so elusive that its very existence has been doubted, we believe that we can recognize degrees of capacity; just as we all know perfectly well that human minds show differing degrees of intelligence. Variation by small steps up and down a scale is a universal phenomenon in all natural objects and events, and when once the possibility of animal mind is recognized, we must be prepared to admit all likely degrees of variation. By this is implied not differences of understanding in the usual sense but differences in response to the same situation, as is shown in the habits of mother wolf-spiders (19) when deprived of their cocoons.

2. The events in the animal mind must be called 'thoughts', for there is no other word for them, unless we invent a new one, such as 'putones', from the Latin *puto,* I think. The existing alternatives, dreams, hopes, desires and so on, are only names for special kinds of thoughts. In the human mind, thoughts are normally expressed in language, and none but the simplest can be developed save with the help of words. It would therefore

seem that animals cannot experience any thoughts save such as present themselves in the form, as it were, of pictures or sensations.

I vividly remember an occasion when this fact was very wisely put before my youthful mind. It was in Brittany, before the First World War, and I had been watching a very familiar-looking snail. I said to my father, 'I wonder if this snail thinks in French or English'. Unhesitatingly he replied, 'I do not suppose that its thoughts need either language', which quite admirably expresses the position.

The animal's putones, pictures or sensations will be solely concerned with the elementals—shelter, food and drink, mates. There must be an extremely narrow margin between an animal that is hungry and an animal that is thinking of food : a margin that is possibly imaginable among invertebrates, though in human beings it is scarcely detectable.

3. It follows that these limitations produce two particularly important differences between the mind of man and the mind of an animal. One of these is the existence of so many ideas which the animal cannot be made to understand, so many situations which the animal cannot grasp. This is not the same sort of inability as the inability of a classical scholar to understand the differential calculus, but a basic failure to comprehend an idea, however presented. A spider which is unable to escape from a box, but which none the less spins a web inside it, failing to realise that flies cannot get in, is an illustration of this limitation. A human being who looks at the stars and cannot grasp the meaning of infinite space or who, having been informed by astronomers that the universe is limited or finite, can form no picture of what exists beyond its boundaries, is also showing a limitation of mind. One of these limitations is common to all spiders, the other to all men.

The second difference is the inability of the invertebrate mind to anticipate, to plan, to design a course of action adapted to a future set of circumstances. A man quickly learns, and a dog learns almost as quickly, to anticipate the course of a rubber ball as it bounces off a perpendicular wall; but a spider never makes a movement which suggests that it anticipates the actions of a fly.

The possibility if not of anticipation at least of a kind of judgment should be included at this point.

Many spiders in their search for food leap upon their victims, particularly the wolf-spiders, which pursue their prey and jump on them, with extreme vigour, at a distance of a couple of inches or so, and the jumping-spiders, which creep up slowly and jump a good deal farther. A jump may be unfruitful, because the insect has flown away in the last fraction of a second, but it is apparently very seldom badly aimed or badly judged.

It follows, therefore, that unless the predator always makes its leap when the prey is at the same distance, that is to say unless it always mechanically, inevitably, makes the same jump in response to the same stimulus (whether it is itself fatigued or hungry or hot), it must possess some power of distance-judging, and some ability to adjust the force with which it leaps to the distance it estimates. If this is so, it is very difficult to believe that such distance-judging and jump-measuring are anything less than the results of a mental operation of some kind : it provides us with a possible source of evidence of the existence of an invertebrate mind, and some source of information as to its nature.

The acceptance of the existence in invertebrate animals of something which can only be described as a mind has an immediate bearing on the biologist's attitude towards the teleological interpretation of animal behaviour. The teleologist's point of view was discussed in Chapter II.

It is, as we have seen, easy to criticize the teleological descriptions of behaviour, and it is in fact almost traditional to do so, and to do so unthinkingly. But the recognition of mind in an animal compels us to admit the indisputable existence of purposes in the mind. If a mind does not formulate purposes, it is acting only as a clearing-house for incoming sensory impulses and outgoing responses, a mechanical process which can be performed even by a few segments of a nerve cord.

The real disadvantage about a truly teleological view of invertebrate behaviour is that it is risky. It is so easy to guess the wrong purpose behind the animal's actions. When, by chance or experience, the correct purpose, with its necessary limitations, is postulated, satisfactory progress is assured.

It is even necessary to be more lenient with descriptions which include descriptions of a mental, or psychical, condition, such as anger or excitement. The arguments by which the mechanist supports his hypothesis usually follow the same familiar lines.

He begins by saying that it is often unwise to imagine that one can tell what thoughts are passing through the mind of one's best friend, and that when for a friend a mosquito or a wood-louse is substituted it is much more difficult, or perhaps it is impossible to do so. The step that follows from this is that it is wiser to assume that the animal has no mind.

Of course to interpret the thoughts, or their equivalent, which determine an animal's behaviour is difficult, but this is no reason for not making an attempt to do so. If it were not difficult, there would be very little interest in the study of animal behaviour, and very few books about it. Even if it is 'impossible' there is no need for a defeatist attitude. During the War our technicians were proud to say 'The incredible we do at once, the impossible takes a little longer', and no scientist ought to admit inferiority to technicians, who make use of the principles that scientists have discovered.

It is valuable to look closely at the idea that we must have no knowledge of the animal mind, and as a vulnerable example I quote a few lines from my own book, *The Arachnida,* in which I discussed a report that a spider had seized a vibrating tuning-fork with considerable excitement, and had walked up it, biting it continually. I wrote, 'It is to be supposed that if we ask this observer why the spider bit the fork so often, the answer will be, "Because it was excited". If we press the matter and ask, "How do you know it was excited?" the only answer can be, "Because it bit the fork often" '. This argument in a circle I assumed to lead nowhere.

It might alternatively be said that the observer saw the spider repeatedly biting the fork: this was visible and indisputable evidence that it was excited bodily. In other words that an imperious stimulus produced a vigorous response. If the spider was a machine, and nothing else, nothing more than its bodily tissues and organs can have been excited, because there was nothing more to stimulate. Therefore it was true that the spider was excited.

If a spider is a psychosome, or a combination of a body and a mind, it is difficult to be equally sure that the spider's mind is excited, but only because it is difficult to conceive how events in the body can be translated into sensations in the mind. But such a difficulty is not evidence that there is no connection or relation between the two.

Excitement, like many other phenomena, has both a subjective and an objective side. A child excited on Christmas Eve by an anticipation of pleasure on the morrow is an example of pure subjective excitement. I find it impossible to believe that a state of this kind can exist in the central nervous system of a spider; that, having spun its web it is excited at the prospect of catching a fly.

A group of glands secreting saliva or semen or silk are accurately described as excited in an objective sense, and by synecdoche the animal possessing the glands is said to be excited. This at once confuses the issue, not biologically but verbally, because of the associations of the word 'excited'. The risk of confusion would be reduced if in this case the word 'stimulated' were used instead.

Among human beings, where we are sure of a dual relation between mind and body, such that each can affect the other, it is clear that mental excitement can act as a stimulus to the body and also that a physical stimulus can produce mental excitement, and with other mammals the case is not significantly different. But among invertebrates it is different, and this is because we seldom know how to interpret the physical evidence of its mental state. We know that a dog is excited by something on the other side of a closed door, and we can interpret his bark and his scratching on the panel; but we seldom get equally comprehensible evidence of mental excitement in a snail or a scorpion. Yet as long as we reject the idea that even an invertebrate is a mere organic machine and nothing more, we must be ready to admit the possibility that a stimulated body may accompany an excited mind. If is, in fact, far less reasonable to deny it.

It is therefore quite valueless to say that we can gain no direct knowledge of the nature of the animal's mind. Even if it were true, which may be argued, since it depends on what is meant by 'direct', it only leads us to the necessity of supposing an animal mind to exist. That is to say, we must enunciate a hypothesis to this effect; and in the scientific method a hypothesis is used not because it is necessarily true, but because it is helpful.

IX

INVERTEBRATE BEHAVIOUR

Biologists who study the smallest animals and plants find, when they examine the class Flagellata or Mastigophora, that the traditional distinction between animals and plants cannot be maintained. They find species which show the characteristics of both kinds or organisms, and they can arrange a series of chosen species in such a way as to show so smooth a gradation from typical plant to typical animal that it is impossible, save by arbitrary convention, to say at which stage the change from plant to animal occurs. They conclude that the Protista over which they are puzzling are the descendants of primitive organisms living at a time when there was no such thing as a plant, no such thing as an animal.

Yet later the distinction is clear enough, and the zoologist and botanist are investigating two quite different kinds of organisms, which have evolved along different yet parallel paths. In other words, the two great groups of living things establish the principle of parallelism in evolutionary biology. No one can suggest that animals are more highly evolved than plants, or vice versa; nor that animals are descended from plants, or vice versa. Yet there are many ways in which animals and plants resemble each other, over and above the fact that both are composed of protoplasm and that both liberate energy by respiration. In both the animal and plant kingdoms there has occurred the production of the cellular body, increase in size, establishment of sexual reproduction by gametes, invasion of the land, appearance of parasitic forms, and so on. All these things have taken place independently; sex in animals owes nothing to sex in plants; liverworts and ferns are not related to amphibians and reptiles, although they typify comparable stages in the evolution of terrestrial life.

These ideas establish the principle of parallelism in evolution, and the frequency with which it occurs deserves emphasis. The whole argument of this chapter depends on it.

Within the animal kingdom itself, this parallelism is equally conspicious. The phyla Annelida, Mollusca and Arthropoda form one group of animals, while the phyla Echinmodermata and Chordata form another. Between the two there are many similarities, points of apparent resemblance which can only be described as instances of parallel evolution. The repetition of parts or metameric segmentation found in the earthworm is superfically similar to the series of muscles in the body of Amphioxus, but the two appearances of segmentation are quite independent. The power of flight has already been mentioned as a capacity found in certain groups of both invertebrates and vertebrates, but it is unrelated in the two groups. So too, both invertebrates and vertebrates have had to meet the dangers which appear when life on land replaces life in water, and have overcome them in quite different ways.

Because both types of animals nourish themselves holozoically, spending energy in the process, and because they live side by side in the same surroundings, there can be no surprise that there is a close superficial resemblance between their behaviour patterns. Hibernation, courtship, parental care, for example, are found in both groups, for both are adapted to survive in the same environment and conquer in the same struggle for existence.

Thus it has come about that the tacit assumption has been made that there is a topic or subject or part of zoology to be called animal behaviour and to be studied as a homogeneous whole. But of course this is no more true than the idea that animal morphology must be so studied. Every course in morphology has a half which proceeds from Amoeba to insects and a half which proceeds from Amphioxus to mammals, and from the point of view of the student it is completely immaterial which half is taken first.

The preceding chapters of this book have described a number of forms of behaviour shown by invertebrates and it is the purpose of this final section to survey them and at the same time to show in how many ways their behaviour is different from that of vertebrates. There are, of course, resemblances, but these are superficial or apparent; they are no more than instances of the universal parallelism which has just been shown to exist as a general principle in evolution. The differences are far more important; they are more significant, more fundamental in character, and taken together they prove conclusively that invertebrate behaviour has a relation to that of vertebrates which is more misleading than real. These differences will, for convenience and emphasis, be put down in a numbered series.

1. Invertebrate behaviour as a whole is more varied than vertebrate behaviour. This is partly because the body of an invertebrate responds more readily to many stimuli than does the body of a vertebrate, having a specialized sensory equipment which vertebrates lack. For example, the many setae with which the bodies of insects and arachnids are often clothed are far more sensitive even than the whiskers of a cat. The most delicate, the trichobothria, are apparently able to detect the vibrations of the air which constitute sound waves (Fig. 15). Partly the more

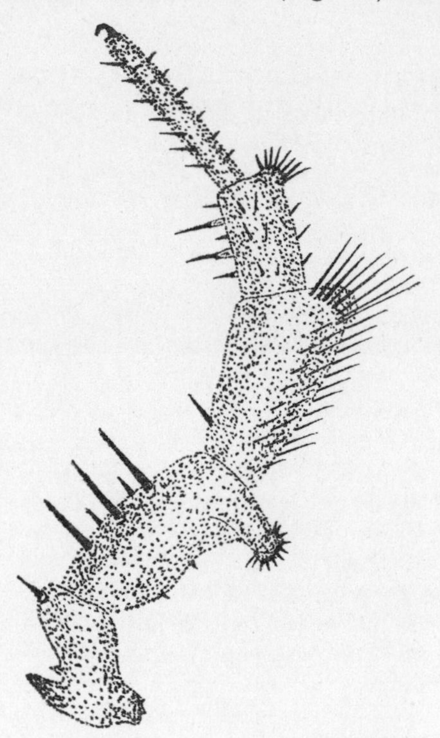

FIG. 15. Pedipalp of a harvestman (Megabunus), illustrating the variety of spines and setae, with different groupings and probably different sensitivities.

varied nature of invertebrate behaviour is due to the ability to respond to stimuli to which a vertebrate is all but indifferent.

Vibrations of the ground and the hygrometric state of the air are two examples which have been mentioned in earlier chapters; another is the response to polarization of light, which does not affect men or dogs in the way it affects ants and bees.

2. The behaviour which is called reflex action is more extensive among invertebrates and is more significant in their daily lives. Invertebrates show a tendency to develop one particular reflex, which becomes a dominant form of response: the flexor reflex of the forelegs has been mentioned above as an example of a reflex which is the basis of a variety of devices for favouring survival. Further, the reflexes of invertebrates appear to be difficult to condition in the way that conditioned reflexes arise in the vertebrates.

3. The directed reflexes or tropisms are typically invertebrate reactions. All the most fruitful work of Loeb and his school was done on invertebrate subjects such as coelenterates or barnacle larvae. The so-called tropisms of vertebrates, which in modern nomenclature are designated as taxes or kineses, are fundamentally of a different character. The precision of the mathematical behaviour of invertebrates, which can be shown to be acting in agreement with an algebraic formula, is not to be found among backboned animals. To speak of the tropisms of vertebrates is to attempt to force observed behaviour into a preconceived classification.

4. Rhythmic behaviour is more typically invertebrate. Rhythms may indeed appear among vertebrates, but clearly they are not so deeply impressed on the organism nor so necessarily obeyed; nor do they possess the same ecological significance, nor play as valuable a part in securing survival.

5. Instinctive actions are devoid of any power to forsee or to anticipate responses on the part of the organism. The instinct-controlled animal is essentially a utilitarian in the sense explained by J. S. Mill, when he argued that men do what they think will give them the greatest satisfaction at the moment. One of the famous Public Schools of England has as its motto the words *Sapiens qui prospicit,* a phrase which, though not chosen with any such intention, biologically distinguishes man, boy, and a very few other mammals from all invertebrates.

In addition to the normal concern of all instinctive actions with protection, feeding and reproduction, the instinctive actions of invertebrates show a capacity for construction, an ability to collect and use, or to secret and use, materials of all sorts to a degree which is not approachd by the vertebrates.

The early steps in this constructive ability are seen in the simple secretion of tubes or shells round the body, then in the making of such tubes from collected matter, as in the cases of the caddis-fly larvae, and then in a true manipulation of material, making such things as egg-cocoons, rest-cocoons, spiders' webs, bees' combs and termites' cities, all far in advance of beavers' dams or birds' nests.

* * * *

Our dogs sleep, and manifestly dream much as we do ourselves. Sleep is a necessity for vertebrates; its interruption, if frequent, is one of the most brutal forms of torture, and it has been stated that complete prevention of sleep is more rapidly fatal than starvation. Invertebrates do not appear to sleep or to show any difference between a state of conscious activity and a state of unconscious repose: the necessity for a suspension of operations does not seem to be felt by a solid, ganglionated, nervous system. The alternative point of view, sometimes expressed, that invertebrates are always asleep and never wake up, depends only on definitions, and is but another way of saying the same thing.

Our dogs show evidence of anger, affection, misery, desire, and many other emotions, which we human beings share and can recognise in them. Many cautious biologists choose to be very sceptical about accepting the visible evidence of the emotions of a dog or a cat, from which one can only assume that they have never been the owners of such animals. Those who have know well enough that vertebrates will respond to our own feelings, and that often they do so even before the tone of our voice has suggested our mood. A telepathic communication between a man and his dog is believed by many to have come within their experience. Nothing of this sort is possible with invertebrates. Spiders have been kept and fed by the same person for years, with no evidence of so much as individual recognition. The matter was well put by Tilquin (22), who had large numbers of spiders in his care during his work on the orb-web, when he wrote:

'L'Homme pour l'Araignée n'est qu'une silhouette qui affecte sa vue, une masse qui affecte son sens tactile ou vibratoire, un corps chaud qui affecte son sens thermique.' (For a spider a man is only a shadow which affects its vision, a mass which affects its tactile or vibratory sense, a warm thing which affects its thermal sense.)

Further, there are some who possess a wonderful power of communication with animals, and therefore it is interesting to ask whether such unusually gifted persons have ever found an invertebrate responding in anything like the way a dog can respond. Readers of the books of Mrs. Barbara Woodhouse will agree that if anyone could talk to an insect or an arachnid, she should be able to do so. In reply to my questioning, she wrote, 'I have never found there to be any intelligent communication possible between me and invertebrates in the same way as with vertebrates'.

This book suggests that in effect there are no animals which are completely mechanical devices, but that in all of them there is something, let it be repeated, 'that corresponds to the origin of thoughts in man'. If this view is not accepted the implication is that the animal kingdom must be divided into animals without minds and animals with minds, with the inevitable question, where is the line to be drawn ?

The suggestion behind this question was always the unexpressed belief that the line must be a horizontal one, with some animals below it and others above it. The alternative, developed however imperfectly in this book, is that the line is a vertical one, and that on one side are the animals with ganglia and solid nerve cords, on the other are those with brains and hollow nerve cords. Both kinds have found survival possible in a world that offers them little encouragement, but rather violence and sudden death. And when we look critically at the struggle for existence, we perceive that among animals on one side of the line the tendency is for the mind to take care of the body, while on the other the invertebrate body takes care of the mind.

If one can imagine the human race being observed and discussed by insects—and the idea is no more improbable than that they should be observed and discussed by the occupants of flying saucers—one can visualize the animals as criticising with caustic contempt our method of conducting our affairs in the light of a muddled intelligence. 'Just fancy', one ant would say to another, 'being in doubt as to what to do, and not knowing inside yourself exactly when to start a new job!' 'Imagine,' an earwig would say to a millipede, 'finding yourself faced by alternatives, and having to hestitate, while you decided which course to take.'

'Do you mean to say,' a young bee would ask its mentor, 'that sometimes these human beings do not know what to do next?' 'Next,' replies the older bee with scorn, 'I don't think they even know what they are doing now.' 'I wonder, then,' concludes the young bee, 'whether they can be asked to explain why they spend so much time and thought in studying the arts of Arachne.'

BIBLIOGRAPHY

1. BARROWS, W. M. (1915). The Reactions of an Orb-weaving Spider to Rhythmic Vibrations of its Web. *Biol. Bull.*, Vol.29, pp. 316–332.
2. BERLAND, L. (1945). *Les Scorpions.*
3. BIERENS DE HAAN, J. (1931). *Die Tierischeinstinkt.*
4. BLUMENTHAL, H. (1935). Untersuchungen uber das 'Tarsalorgan' der Spinnen. *Zeits. Morphol. Okol. Tiers.*, Vol. 29, pp. 667–719.
5. BONNET, P. (1930). La mue, l'autotomie et la rgeneration chez les Araignees. *These Fac. sci. Toulouse.* Vol. 44, pp. 1–464.
6. BRISTOWE, W. S. (1947). *Spiders.*
7. CLOUDSLEY-THOMPSON, J. L. (1950). The water-relations and cuticle of Paradesmus. *Quart. J. Micr. Sci.*, Vol. 91, pp. 453–464.
8. CLOUDSLEY-THOMPSON, J. L. (1952). Changes in the physiological responses of the woodlouse to environmental stimuli. *J. Exper. Biol.*, Vol. 29, pp. 295–303.
9. CLOUDSLEY-THOMPSON, J. L. (1953). Photoperiodism in the Cockroach Periplaneta. *Ann. Mag. Nat. Hist.* (12), Vol. 6, pp. 705–712.
10. COOKE, A. H. (1895). 'Molluscs', in *The Cambridge Natural History*, Vol. 3.
11. EDNEY, E. B. (1953). The Woodlice of Great Britain and Ireland. *Proc. Linn. Soc.*, Vol. 164.
12. FRAENKEL, J. and GUNN, D. L. (1940). *The Orientation of Animals.*
13. GUNN, D. L. (1934). Temperature and Humidity Relations of the Cockroach. *Zeits. Morphol. Okol. Tiers.*, Vol. 28, pp. 617–625.
14. HOLZAPFEL, M. (1933). Die nicht-optische Orientierung der Trichterspinne Agelena. *Zeits. vergl. Physiol.*, Vol. 20, pp. 55–116.
15. JOAD, C. E. M. (1928). *The Meaning of Life.*
16. KASTON, B. J. (1936). The Senses used in the Courtship of some Vagabond Spiders. *Ent. Amer.*, Vol. 16, pp. 97–167.
17. MORLEY, D. W. (1953). *The Ant World.*
18. RUSSELL, E. S. (1938). *The Behaviour of Animals.*
19. SAVORY, T. H. (1929). On Wolf-Wolf-Spiders Memories. *Ann. Mag. Nat. Hist.* (10), Vol. 4, pp. 524–528.
20. SAVORY, T. H. Notes on the Biology of Arachnida, III. *J. Quek. Micr. Cl.* (4), Vol. 3, pp. 448–452.

21. Thomas, M. (1952). Observations sur Lycosa radiata. *Bull. et Ann. Soc. Ent. Belg.*, Vol. 88, pp. 82–90.
22. Tilquin, A. (1942). *La Toile Geometrique.*
23. Tinbergen, N. (1951). *The Study of Instinct.*
24. Wood, T. (1863). *Natural History*, Vol. 3, p. 677.

INDEX